A Secret Life

A journey through the trials of physical deformity and deep depression. A story of human courage, loneliness, enlightenment and joy.

Written by

Greg Ryan

Film, Books Anything
2019

All profits support the work of the Onein5000 Foundation.

Second Edition.
Printed in 2019
Copyright Greg Ryan.

ISBN: 978-0-6481024-2-7

Photos: The Ryan Family

Cover Photo: Katerina Foskolou (Greece)
http://pendulumphotography.deviantart.com

Cover Graphic Design: Tahlia West
tahlia@tagraphicdesign.com.au

Proudly Published by Film, Books, Anything Pty Ltd (Australia)

A Warning

You may find some of the content of my autobiography confronting but telling my story truthfully has required revisiting details that confuse us all. My story links my congenital birth defect with my mental health.

I was born with a rare congenital condition called an Imperforate Anus (IA), also known as Anorectal Malformation (ARM). In short, I was born without an anal opening and had no functioning sphincter muscles as well as associated Genito-Urinary issues. This congenital anomaly occurs in 1:5000 births and requires immediate medical intervention at birth. There are varying types of IA/ARM and in my case, I was diagnosed with a very rare type with an incidence rate of less than 5% of IA/ARM cases.

I have been blessed with the support of others but I have struggled to make sense of my life's circumstances. Hopefully my narrative reminds the reader that too many of us carry the burden of being outsiders.

Thank you to my incredible mum & dad. I struggle to find the right words to describe their love and support. Thanks also to my brother Brad, his wife Peta, their beautiful boys Archer & Jack, my extended family, my friends and the North Melbourne Football Club.

Your generosity has saved me in my darkest hours.
"Sometimes the things we can't change end up changing us."
Anonymous

Preface

Greg Ryan and I had been friends for nearly 5 years before he could tell me his secret. I had been aware of his emotional and mental struggles but had no understanding of the root cause. This book uncovers that cause. We think Greg's is the first memoir which addresses a congenital illness that has existed through human history.

It has been my honour to know Greg and his family and to help publish this book in various countries of the world. It has been a whirlwind ride because Greg's courageous and honest story has touched the hearts of many. It has been an eye-opener and resource for those who support the survivors: the families, the doctors, the welfare agencies and the schools.

I have watched, along with other advisory committee members, Greg grow into a leadership role that has seen the ONE in 5000 Foundation influence thinking in many countries. Greg's tireless work on social media has meant that the story has brought attention to the needs of survivors of IA/ARM without breaching privacy. Greg tells his own story simply and well but in this second edition also adds several other components which will hopefully inspire others to continue what Greg's work has started. I know he draws great strength from many people in maintaining equilibrium, but I pay tribute to the support of Senator Anne Urquhart, Bert Newton, Dr Sebastian King, Chelsea Mullins and Greg's Facebook communities.

Les Cameron Publisher 2019

Introduction

Do you remember that uncomfortable feeling in your stomach when you must race off to the toilet? Or the time when you just sit there in frustration, willing yourself to any bowel movement? When this happens, your preference is that you are in the safety and privacy of your own home. If you are at work, or out for dinner, or at the movies, or doing something recreational it is much harder to cope.

If this only happened once or twice a year that would certainly be once or twice too many. Can you imagine facing this scenario every day of your life? Just how would you manage?

Due to my congenital condition, I face this reality each day as do many others across the world. Because of the nature of its affects it is something that is seldom discussed due to the stigma attached to our toilet habits.

It is so personal and taboo in all cultures that our bowel functions are the last topic anyone wants to discuss. From my earliest memory, I have chosen to keep my condition as my secret. Only my parents and doctors were aware of my trauma. The thought that anyone else would know was too embarrassing and humiliating for me to bear.

So, I learnt to live my life doing everything I could to protect my secret from ever being known. I now know that came at a huge cost. The toll that living with my secret would take on me on a physical and emotional level is addressed in this story. For most readers, it will be incredibly confronting, but hopefully educational and maybe inspirational as well.

My coming out has been stressful and damaging but I hope this book can break down the walls for others who have lived with this condition. I trust it assists those families, friends, lovers and medicos who care for IA survivors to get a greater insight into how living with this disability could be better managed.

I was fortunate to be able to obtain all my medical records (which run to almost 400 pages) from the 20 years I spent as a patient of the Melbourne Royal Children's Hospital and I have referred regularly to selected surgery reports, medical correspondence and other records that I believe will add to the story of living a secret life.

I recognise now that my story is shared by many. Everyone who lives with a disability, a trauma or tremendous disadvantage will recognise themselves in these pages. The fight to be normal, to avoid sinking into depression and to find kindness in others is challenging. Surviving is difficult and secrecy has been my curse.

I hope these words can help those who have also drawn a curtain around their lives.

Greg Ryan

Chapter 1 - Finding my Voice

I was struggling to adjust to the reality of my new life and my wonderful Psychiatrist Dr. Hocking suggested I start to write when I felt anxious and vulnerable. He believed it would be therapeutic for me and he encouraged me to bring my writings to each appointment. He found new insights into my life and I found new perspectives.

On the 20st December 2010, I received a phone call from the NMFC CEO to advise me that the club was to bestow a Special Services Award to me as recognition of my contribution to the Club. I was touched and honored and especially pleased to advise mum & dad who were extremely proud.

I received my Award at the NMFC Annual General Meeting. There were over 500 people in attendance and I was extremely anxious, but somehow, managed my acceptance speech. I spoke for about five minutes and was able to express myself in the way I had hoped. My emotions were only just under control as I exalted my parents, the club and the close personal friends that had supported me. I was overwhelmed by the number of people who congratulated me on the award (and on my speech).

I woke the next day with a weird feeling. I knew that a crucial chapter of my life had now been closed and that the award had diminished my shame. But I felt empty and low. Within days I had spun so far out of control that I resorted again to self-harm. Another deep cut re-opened the scar as conflicting emotions of pride and shame flooded through my body.

Over the next few months my wonderful Nan died and my venerable and my life saving, faithful Psychiatrist, Dr. Hocking retired. The combined affect was desolating. I realize that I had worshipped them both and their amazing support and kindness was now gone. Stupidly, I understand now, I booked a holiday to Bali to help me cope with the loss. It was a monstrous disaster immediately.

Just before flight time I had a bowel accident. There was no time to properly clean myself. Travelling for five hours knowing I was a hygienic mess was beyond my ability to cope.

I only lasted in Bali for three days before I   cut short my holiday. I returned in disarray, both physically and mentally. For several months, I lived in a torpor of despair and isolation; regularly mutilating myself and searching for some pathway out. My parents must have lived the worst moments since my birth as they watched my descent.

Somewhere in that suffocating haze I commanded a search on Facebook for "Imperforate Anus". I was hoping there may be a support group for people with the condition. I was delighted when

I found there were three separate private groups accessible. I immediately introduced myself to each and noted that I lived in Melbourne, Australia.

Within 24 hours I received a message from a woman who lived in Melbourne who was a mum of an IA son. She was also an organizer of an Imperforate Anus Support Group. She advised me there were five other members of the group who lived in Melbourne. I had been thinking all my life that I wouldn't know anyone else with IA and now within minutes I had 5 instant contacts. I was amazed and delighted.

The Melbourne group had decided it was time for the mums and their kids to meet each other. I knew how much that would mean. Apparently, I was so open in my introduction to the Facebook group and so willing to share my personal experiences they were gracious enough to invite me to their next meet up. It was to be at the Melbourne Zoo.

I arrived at the Zoo gates feeling apprehensive but excited at the same time. I met the group who were just inside the gate and they greeted me with great enthusiasm which settled me. There were four mums and their kids, which included   non-IA youngsters as well. For the first hour, we just strolled through the Zoo and chatted casually but awkwardly.

Eventually over lunch the inevitable conversation began. One of the mums described the history of her then seven-year-old son. She explained how her son required daily enemas. I was overcome by a wave of emotion. As I watched this wonderful kid enjoy the company of his peers I saw myself. There was a feeling of sadness; a feeling of anxiousness; a feeling of sorrow; a feeling of protection; a feeling of pain and the overwhelming feeling of hope. I had to do everything in my power not to burst into tears!

Minutes later, still bemused, I began to talk to another of the mothers. Her name was Christi, and I eventually asked how her daughter was, wondering if she had required the same debilitating treatment that I so well remembered as a child. She paused and I immediately thought I had said the wrong thing. Seconds later she haltingly revealed: "It's not my daughter Greg, I am the one who has IA."

I was speechless and tears ran down our faces. It was the first time either of us had ever met another Adult with IA. We both have lived a lifetime of thinking we were the only person in the world with the condition. If I thought what had happened only a few minutes earlier was incomprehensible then this news burst across my soul. I am not alone anymore!

From that moment, my life took another dramatic turn. Quickly I began to link all over the world with others disabled by IA. There were long and short conversations, messages and exchanges across the vast loneliness of our separated lives. I shared anecdotes, tears and therapies each time recognizing the levels of despair and self-disgust that we had experienced. I learnt from a wonderful contact in Britain (Chrissy) who also had IA to think of myself as a survivor rather than a victim of this fluke of fate.

Somehow, I began to feel both validated and vindicated enough to face both the past and the future with purpose.

The more we have chatted the more we found that our lives had mirrored each other in so many ways. In all facets, we seemed to have lived the same life, from the relationships we have with our parents, to the issues we had at school, to the adjustment to becoming an adolescent and finding our own way to deal with the condition daily as an adult. We had similar experiences with relationships with the opposite sex, with our lack of self-esteem and the embarrassment we had with our bodies.

Then when it came to the stage where we had to go out into the world and start working, we both had to deal with the same difficulties. To deal with our incontinence issues etc. and planning our days to ensure that our condition didn't have a detrimental effect on our work performance. Then trying so hard to be a normal person and not let on to others how much of a toll our condition was taking on us emotionally and physically each day.

The more we chatted the more we realized that we could be totally at ease with each other and acknowledge our shame and secrecy. I had had to rely on my medical advisors, parents and partners over the years. They had tried to understand what I lived but I had found others now who totally empathized.

Over the days and weeks that followed I realized that I needed another change. I needed to give voice to my doubts and my confidences. I need to feel free to speak about the problem with everyone and to share the idea that all of us who had Imperforate Anus disability could overcome the doubts and degradation with the appropriate support and honesty.

I have thoroughly enjoyed exchanging life experiences with the group and the feedback I have received has been overwhelmingly positive. I have developed close bonds with some parents by sharing my experiences, and been advised that I have changed many parents outlook as to how they might deal with their child's life. I have been able to give them insights that they could not get from their Doctors. I now say to any parent who asks me any questions, "I am your child's voice". I am clear that has been an important role.

On the 30th October 2014, I decided to take control of something in my life once again and give myself a purpose. I created a brand-new group on Facebook called "Adults Living with Imperforate Anus". It is a group specifically designed to cater for IA Adults only. Over these months I have helped develop a dynamic and thoughtful small network of IA Adults through the online International Imperforate Anus Support Group.

I decided to create the IA Adults only group to give all IA Adults an avenue to be able to discuss issues in an open and supportive environment, but most importantly not feel like they need to filter anything they say which happens in the parents' group. Each IA Adult I had met online since I joined the group had the same experience as I, not having met anyone else with IA before they found our group on Facebook.

I created the group as a secret group which means that everyone's privacy is respected. People join the group by invitation after strict protocols and relevant checks are made. I finally felt I had something where I had a reason to get up each morning. I felt energized and passionate to make this work.

I have built friendships over the last year that mean as much to me now as lifelong friends. I have also been inspired by IA parents who have inspired me with their courage and endless effort to make life for their child as normal as they can. It has given me an even greater appreciation of what my own parents had to endure to ensure my survival as a baby and toddler and into my school and adult years.

Chapter 2 - A Traumatic Birth

I was born at 3.30pm on Saturday 9th May 1964, the first child to my parents, Max & Wendy Ryan. As I was slow to breathe Dr. James Smibert had performed a more thorough examination and exposed my situation.

Minutes after facilitating my birth, Dr. Smibert broke the devastating news to my 21-year-old mother and my 23-year-old father that their newly born son was born with an Imperforate Anus (IA), also known as an Anorectal Malformation (ARM). I was born without an anal opening.

Of course, it was life-threatening and needed to be treated immediately.

My shocked and distraught parents had absolutely no idea what this condition was, and were even more distraught when advised by Dr. Smibert that it would be prudent to arrange that I be baptized as soon as possible. Due to my condition, there was no certainty at that time that I would survive the day.

Within minutes my parents had gone from the absolute joy of their first child being born to the absolute horror of being told he may not survive. I was baptized in my Mother's arms an hour after I was born and then placed in a Humidi-Crib. I was then rushed, in the back seat of my Fathers Volkswagen, accompanied by a Nurse, to the Melbourne Royal Children's Hospital (RCH) and was admitted at 5.15pm, less than two hours after I was born.

I now wonder how dad could have had the will to make that drive. It must have been as traumatic for my extended family once the shocking news of my condition was advised. In the ensuing years, all became crucially important to my life. They not only supported my parents but also spent countless hours attending me in hospital.

Ironically, I was later advised by my dad that on this 15-minute journey to the RCH the radio was tuned to North Melbourne playing Hawthorn at our Arden Street Oval. Within hours of being born and with the possibility of immediate death hanging over me the North Melbourne Football Club was being inserted into my psyche.

For dad, a passionate North man, a much more chilling moment was ahead. As I was admitted to the RCH fewer than three hours after I was born, he was required to sign a Parents Authority form saying:

1. High Imperforate Anus without Fistula – No sign of a dimple
2. An abnormality of the Penis
3. Undescended Testes (Right & Left) in Scrotum
4. Bilateral Reflux of Kidneys
5. Joined 4th & 5th toes on Right Foot
6. 6 Lumbar Vertebrae (An extra one, normal 5)

"I, Daniel Maxwell Ryan with full knowledge of the risks involved, give permission for an anesthetic to be administered to Gregory Ryan and for a Medical Officer to give treatment and perform tests and operations. I accept the risks entailed in these procedures."

After dad signed the form an examination was performed and I was diagnosed with a list of medical problems in addition to my Imperforate Anus that must have made him and mum despair.

Within twenty-four hours I was having Traverse Colostomy surgery performed by Surgeon Mr. Nate Myers to enable my body to function. The surgery involved having two openings created in my stomach. Because I did not have an anal opening and had no functioning sphincter muscles. I could only release my faeces through the stomach openings.

I was in hospital for the first 34 days of my life. At that time, my parents could not have imagined that they would still be accompanying me to RCH 20 years later. This was the first of many operations I would endure as a child, and that surgery would continue to shape the person I am today. In simple terms, the consequences of my toilet habits are something I must confront every day. Mum's words to describe how she and dad must have struggled with my initial surgeries and treatment still ring in my ears:

"When he was born my own family doctor (Dr James Smibert) who also delivered Greg came to me and said "We've a few problems with your boy. He has an Imperforate Anus, which means he doesn't have an opening for his bowel. He also has other related problems which we don't understand at the moment. We are sending him to the Children's Hospital to the best man we know in the field. Your baby will be well looked after".

Medical staff asked if we would like to get him baptized and we understood then that our first baby's life was under threat. As we are Catholic's this was critically important to us and of course Max and I said yes. A nurse from the Jessie McPherson Hospital baptised our little boy immediately and then he was taken away. Under the rules that were in place I wasn't allowed to see him for seven days and of course we were worried sick. When I was called in a week later, I looked at the little baby in the Humidi-crib and I declared "that's not my baby". In the first week of his life I had only seen him for an hour, and as a first-time mother I didn't know what to expect.

After he had been there for six weeks of therapies that we did not understand we were given a dire description of his likely future and asked, "Do you want to take him home or do you want us to look after him?" We understood immediately what they were suggesting, and I cried "no, he's my baby and I want him with me no matter what".

We then took him home with his Colostomy. I didn't know what it was, and the description I had from the hospital fell on my deaf ears. Greg had that colostomy for two years as we struggled to keep him alive and learn as much as we could.

As a little baby the Colostomy would burn the skin around his tummy. We had to manage to put cream on the outside of the bowel opening into his stomach and then use gauze and padding to wrap a binder around his body. I used nappies cut into narrow strips bound around his stomach and body to protect the open area.

We changed the binder every time he used his bowels, which was often during each day. Occasionally when it got very severe Greg would experience a burning irritation around the bowel opening and we would have you expose it to the air to heal. I would have to put him in a cot by a window and tie his little hands

down so he wouldn't scratch himself and bleed. Obviously as a mother that was horrific. Sometimes it would get so bad we would have to return to the hospital. I couldn't sleep for these first years *as he would projectile vomit every two hours or so, and I would have to change every stitch of clothing.*

Later, Greg had his surgery to create his bowel opening. It was very difficult initially as I had to perform the "dilations" to keep his new opening open. This required me using my fingers which seemed such an invasion. But I knew I had to do it.

Somehow Max and I got through these difficult early years as privately as we could, but I think the hardest age was when Greg went to school for the first time. Now we had to give him constant enema's and bowel washouts because he would get very constipated. There were many times when the school would call me to tell me he had had an accident and we remember both walking home crying and distressed about what was happening to us.

We knew Greg was a very special child and it's awful what he had to deal with but through all the treatments he never cried or never complained; he would just lie on the bed and let me do what I had to do.

I was a first-time mother, and only 21, but somehow we survived and he has grown into a man of such dignity. We are very proud of him!!"

I can't begin to imagine how hard that would have been for my parents: having my bodily functions come out through my stomach. It's a topic that I just can't contemplate discussing in any detail, both from the thought of me having the colostomy plus the trauma I must have caused them in having to deal with this daily for the first two years of my life.

Eighteen months after I was born I had "Anorectoplasty" surgery (which is more commonly called the "Pull Through" Surgery) performed by my doctors. Mr. Myers and Mr. Stephens pulled down my rectum and connected it to my newly created anal opening. The surgery went for over 3 hours and during it, I had to also have a part of my Coccyx removed.

I subsequently spent 22 days in hospital recovering from the surgery, but during that time my parents had to face one of the most distressing and confronting aspects of my condition and that was dealing with having

Dear Nate,

This is a very rare group and I must say that I am not speaking from a wealth of experience, but I have been most interested in this particular abnormality and patients like this are indeed a RARITY".

F. Douglas Stephens
Dept. of Surgical Research
Royal Children's Hospital

NB: Mr. Stephens co-authored a book in 1971 called "Ano-Rectal Malformations in Children" which at the time was recognised worldwide in the Colorectal Pediatric community as the most comprehensive written work on my condition.

to perform manual "Anal Dilations" on my newly created anal opening. The dilations were necessary to prevent the anal opening from narrowing.

Progressively, I would get to a stage where my surgeons were satisfied I could pass stools through my newly created bottom, and then they could perform the closure of colostomy surgery.

The anxiety of my first two years and the regular impacts on my body left more than scars. In my first three years, I had major surgeries requiring a total of 89 days in hospital plus numerous visits to the Emergency Room when I required urgent attention. By the end of March 1966, my parents were advised that the three major surgeries which were required for my Imperforate Anus had been completed. There were to be other surgeries to come in the future for my unresolved genital issues but my parents must have been relieved that the worst seemed to be over.

Dear Sirs

We would like to convey to you and your associates our sincere thanks and appreciation for the marvelous and humane consideration that has been shown by all at the Hospital in respect to our son Greg since the initial entrance to the Hospital concerning his well-being and health, once again thanking you one an all.

The Ryan Family

Their relief was expressed in a formal way in a letter dated 29th March 1966 to Mr. Myers & Mr. Stephens.

Over the ensuing 12 months, I had only a couple of visits to the Hospital, as my parents could look after me by performing rectal enemas, bowel washouts and by using appropriate laxatives. These days it is common to describe this list of activities as a Bowel Management Program, but that expression was not noted at all in any of my Medical records. Although the major interventions were completed there were still issues that needed to be surgically addressed and the Doctors were happy for me to have a break.

During this break, my brother Brad was born and thankfully Brad was born with ten toes (I only had nine) and ten fingers but more importantly he was born with a normal anal opening and both testes were present. I can only imagine how much of a relief this must have been for my parents. To have a healthy baby this time around would enable them to celebrate the birth of a son as a totally joyous occasion unlike the horrific trauma they had endured at my birth.

Sadly, within three months, I was back in hospital for my next bout of surgery. I was admitted on the 22nd June 1967 and was scheduled to have two further Operations in my 19 day stay. The first of the operations was to deal with what was diagnosed at birth as a *Penile Abnormality* which was then recognized as a sinus on the ventral aspect of the penis.

The surgery was described as an *Excision of Penile Pit and Polyp*. From the records, this seemed to be successful but it was to bring me a lifetime of concern.

The following year I was in RCH having an invasive procedure called a barium enema performed by Mr. Justin Kelly. He noted that I was a *"tearful but co-operative and anxious 4-year-old"*. This was I suspect an accurate analysis as well as a sound prediction of my future. I remember how invasive the procedure was physically but I was in even more mental torment sitting there with doctors and nurses watching me as I tried to pass motions. The thought of it now brings back extremely humiliating memories for me.

In the investigation notes I learnt that I had the *"catheter inserted without resistance"*. I may have not had any resistance at that age, but as the years progressed, the thought of such a procedure was to fill me with the greatest fear and distress.

Chapter 3 - School Daze

I started kindergarten in 1969, and at this stage I was still dealing with major, ongoing daily bowel issues. These ranged from severe constipation and fecal impactions requiring hospital visits to the regular bowel accidents and daily soiling or leakage which caused my clothes to be stained. My mum was administering daily rectal enemas or bowel washouts in an endeavor to assist me to be as normal as I could be, but it must have seemed like a never-ending battle. Even though my bowel surgeries had been completed, I was clearly not repaired.

Having a rectal enema or a more severe bowel washout became part of my life. As much as I hated them, when my bowels wouldn't work, I had no choice. They were painful, and intrusive, but unfortunately, they were needed. I would have to lie there while my guardian angel, my mum, would insert the catheter deep into my already traumatized bottom. As much as I wanted to scream and cry I had no choice but to accept that to feel better I had to endure and accept the enema. I didn't outwardly complain, but inwardly every time I had the procedure it would be taking a toll on me emotionally and mentally.

Mum understood the trauma I had to endure as she had lived it with me every day since the day I was born. Mum hated the idea that I would have to sustain the pain and discomfort and she hated having to give the enemas to me, but she knew all too well that there was no choice.

For my formative years, rectal enemas or bowel washouts were just part of my normal routine and they were always performed by my mum or a nurse in hospital. It was a horrendous procedure and I now imagine how hard it was on mum having to be responsible for performing them. As I would lie on my side, I would always make sure I turned my head so mum could not see the tears in my eyes as she was inserting the catheter. But for me, the worst part for me was the wait afterwards as I just had to lie there in a prone position waiting for it to take effect. Because I had no feeling in my anal area, I couldn't judge by the pains in my stomach, I had to wait until I could feel some liquid or stool release externally from my bottom before I could move off the bed.

I then had to walk gingerly to the toilet with a towel between my legs ensuring that there was no spillage and had to sit on the toilet and wait for my motions to happen. Once I got to the toilet, invariably it would all become too much for me. I would sit on the toilet and cry: I would cry from pain; I would cry from frustration; and then I would cry from an overwhelming feeling of relief that I had emptied my bowels fully.

After I had completed all my motions, I would have to call either mum or dad to come and check the toilet to ensure I had emptied my bowels. I needed them to give me the approval that I was ok again. I developed a special bond with the toilet, even though I was still so young, I knew that I had found my own sanctuary. Literally in the toilet I could let it all out, physically and emotionally and not be judged. No-one other than my toilet knew what I went through. I hear about children having an imaginary friend, but for me, my friend became an object that was real: it was the toilet. No one else could see the relationship, it was my secret friend and as each day went by, the bond developed.

It was the only relationship where I ever felt an equal: I had a "companion" who had no expectations; one minute my worst enemy and the next my best friend. I didn't ever blame my bowels, I always blamed the toilet. Though I would have the daily battles with the Toilet, for me I had no choice but to fight it, as for me to lose to the toilet wasn't an option. I couldn't show any weakness when I walked into the toilet and though I felt fragile and vulnerable around others, when I walked into the toilet I was a different boy: I showed strength and resilience.

When the battle was over, I would walk from the toilet feeling physically and mentally exhausted. Only the toilet and I knew how much it took out of me, but to walk out winning the battle was all that mattered. When I didn't win the battle, I was devastated but I knew I had no choice and would have to prepare for another soon.

To this day I have the same relationship with the Toilet; I can't know what is going to happen when I enter. I am incredibly envious of those who don't give a second thought to fulfilling this natural human function. For me it can never be a normal or natural experience.

In July 1969, I once again was admitted to the RCH, but this time it was because of the enemas not being sufficient for me to move my bowels. I presented at the Emergency Room with "*a huge mass of faeces palpable in my abdomen*" and it was apparently evident that the only way of removing the faeces was by surgical intervention. Mr. Stephens performed the surgery under a general anesthetic and this time my stay in hospital was for six days.

I was discharged with instructions to my mum to perform alternative day washouts at home for the immediate future. It was a worrying sign for my parents because the earlier surgeries were supposed to have fixed the issue.

As a five-year old and despite these bi-daily enemas I was able to attend primary school. The memories I have which disturbs me to this day occurred when I had bowel accidents in class. I can remember one of these incidents as if it was only yesterday. The absolute horror of knowing that I was unable to get to a toilet in time and had no control over what was happening was incredibly traumatic. For me the most embarrassing and humiliating thing was that I distinctly remember a fellow student yelling "hey, what smells so bad here?" I was now the smelly kid. I became known as "poo pants" and that nickname became unforgettable, haunting me continually.

I remember that I just sat there frozen, not knowing what to do. Looking back now I can say that was the first time I can recognize that I suffered a panic attack. All I wanted was to go home and be with my parents, because they understood and made me feel safe. Even as a young child, I look back now and totally understand that I was so aware of being "teased" or "bullied", even though I was unaware of its true meaning.

There were many times in those early years when my mum would have to come to school after me having a bowel accident. Mum sometimes reminds me that we would both walk home in tears.

By the age of six through the use of appropriate laxatives I had learned to manage with infrequent enemas. The most effective purgatives enabled me to keep my bowels active but this meant soiling and mucous leakage was always more of an issue. I would try every day to appear normal. I would attend school, play sports and have as much fun as I could, but as each day passed I became more and more aware that I was indeed different.

By 1970, I was back in Hospital again, but this time it had nothing to do with my bowels, it was to address the issue of both my testes being undescended. This formed part of the Anorectal Malformation classification which included such conditions under the term 'associated issues'. Due to my life threatening Imperforate Anus, my doctors had been focused on correcting that rather than restoring my testes. I had surgery to lower my right testicle, requiring an eight-day stay in hospital and then 12 months later had similar surgery to lower my left testicle. By now I could say that I was a "real" boy.

After this surgery, Mr. Stephens told my parents that I was now finally "fixed" and I would not require any further compulsory surgeries relating to my anorectal malformation. Inside my body, I didn't feel fixed at all, as mum still had to give me periodic enemas and I was still soiling every day with occasional dramatic bowel accidents.

By the end of 1971, I had endured seven surgeries and had spent a total of 143 days in Hospital, along with 65 days in either an Emergency Ward or as an outpatient. I was only seven years of age but I already had endured a total of 208 days as an inpatient or outpatient.

I now had another scar but ironically my seven scars didn't bother me as I felt a sort of status from these surgical memories. I didn't try to hide them, especially the massive one on my stomach, but if anyone asked their causes, I gave an equivocal and mysterious answer. I suppose I was using the scars to help hide the more sordid truth of my condition.

In 1974, at my annual outpatient visit to the RCH, Mr. Stephens advised us that he would be leaving RCH to take up a position in the United States and that I would be now under the care of Mr. Justin Kelly. Mr. Kelly had treated me periodically over the years and was known to my parents and me, but it was very emotional for my mum specially to hear the news of Mr. Stephens's departure. He had been such an amazing support to my parents from the start and without him and Mr. Myers I suspect mum and dad would not have coped.

Even at ten years old, I knew how much he had done for me and how safe I had felt when under his care. To this day, I hold him in my thoughts with great affection. My gratitude towards Mr. Stephens was the start of what was to become such an important factor in my mental health. I maintain an absolute trust and reliance in my doctors. The dependency I feel for those professionals cannot be measured and I have relied on them from the first day of my life.

In February 1975, in my last year of primary school, I took a massive step towards personal liberation by attending a 10-day school summer trip to the Lord Somers Camp. It was the first time I had spent a night away from the safety of home, my grandparents or a hospital.

I hadn't had a sleepover with friends as I was too scared something might happen with my bowels. Although I was excited about the camp I was of course anxiously apprehensive as well, knowing if I had an accident, I just couldn't run home.

The first night I was fine but by the following night I started to become homesick and I cried myself to sleep because I felt so vulnerable. The next day however I managed to enjoy the activities of the camp, but the best thing was that I went to the toilet okay. We were encouraged to write letters to our families, in one of my letters, I wrote, "I haven't been soiling", which demonstrates how my condition was so embedded in my psyche at such an early age.

By the 6th day of the camp, I was terribly home sick and I started to have more bowel problems, so I went to the sick bay, because I didn't want anyone else to know. The nurse called my mum to tell her what had happened and when mum asked to talk to me, I started to cry uncontrollably and begged mum to come get me.

The emotions just poured out, I had tried so hard to be mature, but it had all become too much for me, both physically and emotionally. Mum calmed me and spoke to the nurse, who confirmed I had settled down. Both agreed I should stay another night.

As the next day was a family visit day the nurse re-assured mum that she would keep an eye on me overnight until all my family came to visit. I stayed in sick bay for a couple of hours after the phone call as I felt safe there as I had in hospital wards. But I also had the comfort that I would be seeing my family the next day. I eventually joined in with the other kids for dinner and before bedtime the nurse came to check on me.

I woke the next morning feeling happy because I knew my family would be coming soon. After breakfast, I had free time but I just headed to the front gate and sat waiting for mum and dad to arrive. I didn't have to wait too long until I saw dad's car coming, and much to my delight, both my grandparents were also with them in the car behind. As soon as they saw me they smiled and waved, and I just started to cry.

I ran to the car and all I could say was I'm sorry, but my family was just as relieved to see me, as they knew it was an important step for me to be on my own for the first time. They all hugged me and told me how very proud of me they were that I had lasted as long as I did.

The one thing I knew was that I was going to go home with them that day and they totally understood. Mum spoke to the nurse and camp staff and they agreed it was the best thing for me. So, after six days of stuttering independence, I was on the way home again, feeling safe! I now know it was the formal beginning of a search for security that would haunt me for the rest of my life.

In April 1975, when I had my annual outpatient visit at RCH, this time with Mr. Kelly, mum asked if he could forward a letter detailing my medical history at RCH to Dr. David Dammery who had been our family doctor since I was born and was well versed with my issues.

As I was only visiting RCH and Mr. Kelly as an outpatient on a yearly review basis now, Dr. Dammery was taking a more prominent part of my life. Even though we had been told I was fixed, I was still dealing with the ongoing issues regarding constipation, soiling, fecal incontinence, mucous discharge and of course, my genital issues.

I was definitely in need of continual medical support and Dr. Dammery was about to become an integral part of my life.

The two sentences that horrify me as I subsequently read the letter are stark and distressing.

"His main problem at this stage is a tendency towards severe constipation and redundant anal rectal mucosa tags which will probably need to be excised eventually"

"He is having normal bowel actions at present, and providing a careful watch is kept he seems to be able to lead a normal life."

They standout to me for two reasons. The first is that I didn't have any further childhood surgery regarding anal rectal mucosa, and I have had to deal with this issue ever since and had subsequently had multiple corrective surgeries in my adult life. The second sentence reminds that there was never to be a "normal" life for me.

The first ten years of my life can be described through many examples of my effort and withdrawal. Without my family's love, indulgence and support I would, quite literally, not have survived.

Chapter 4 - Adolescence

By the time I got to high school in 1976 as an 11-year-old I was starting to understand that I was indeed different to other kids and my ferocious *adjust and adapt* mentality had begun to dominate my strategies. My secret life had started. I had confirmed to myself that under no circumstances would I allow anyone to find about my IA condition.

My secret became the most important factor in my life and it was the alarm that woke me each morning and the narcotic that let me sleep every night. I went to bed knowing that I had to keep the taboo topic obscured. I projected as a happy and smiling kid, as my parents wanted me to be, even though I was scared that the shadows would expose me. I dealt with it all publically and would make sure I didn't show weakness around others, but at home around mum, dad and Brad I couldn't hide my secret.

As much as I tried to be normal around Brad who was three years younger, there was no way I could hide the truth. He could see that I was always running to the toilet, having enemas, or heading to hospital or the doctors. It must have been very confusing to him and he must have felt I was getting all the attention from mum. I have no doubt mum has spoken to him over the years about me and my condition, but it wasn't a topic that I discussed with him, even to this day as an adult. To both of us it has been a no-go zone.

In starting high school, I made the first conscious decision in dealing with my condition. According to Mr. Kelly's RCH medical records by 23th March 1976, less than two months after I started at secondary school it was noted "I was occasionally picked on by other kids". I needed strategies to deter any chance of being bullied further or having my secret revealed.

The one sure way I could be exposed was if others could see a stain on my pants. As there was a strict school uniform policy, I could not get away with wearing very dark pants like I did at primary school. The school trousers were a light grey color and of thin material, so it didn't take me long to realize that any soiling would be easily identified. It filled me with fear and anxiety that I could be caught out and my secret revealed at any time.

I quickly made the decision to wear my school jumper around my waist every single day no matter what the weather was, so no one could identify whether I had soiled my pants. I would sit in class without the jumper around my waist and have it draped over the chair, and would always check to see if there was any evidence of staining on the plastic chair once class had finished as invariably there was. I would grab my jumper and put it around my waist before I walked out of the classroom no matter whether if it was 10 degrees or 40 degrees, as it gave me the sense of security that I so badly needed.

By this stage, I was becoming more aware of my condition and getting to know how my body and bowels worked as I tried to become more independent and self-reliant. I suppose as an adolescent I wanted to become my own person.   My parents had always been my saviors. They were my lifeline and without them when I was young I wouldn't have been able to function.

I was not shielded   from doing what all the other normal kids were doing, be it school, parties or sports. I started playing football for Jordy Jets in 1974 just like many other kids. Although the negative aspects of my condition were significant psychologically, physically I could fully participate in many sports and activities. Thanks particularly to the encouragement of my parents, I am proud that I could play competitive Football from the age of 10 through to 18 and could adapt and put my condition to one side.

Through every game I played however I was paranoid that people would see my soiling through my shorts. One trick that I developed from an early stage playing footy was to bend over and grab some mud or dirt and wipe it on the back of my shorts, thus covering any soiling patch that may have come through. As far as I can tell no-one ever knew this, and it was a formidable part of my adjusting to a situation that protected me and my secret. In every game, I would check my shorts at half-time for any trace of soiling and would always have a spare pair of underpants and shorts.

There was however an upside to my IA, and that was if at any time my courage was questioned I would just lift my footy jersey and show them my massive scar on my stomach. The other advantage was if I was barracked after missing a shot for goal, I could say, "You try and kick straight with only four toes"!

When it came time to play competitive cricket it was a different situation as I had to wear white pants. I was extremely wary of how I would cope and it took me a long time to commit myself. Whereas I started playing footy at the age of ten, I didn't commence competitive cricket until I was 15. I loved playing cricket in the court at home with my neighbours and friends where it was safe for me, as I could wear dark pants or shorts and know that I could just walk inside and change if needed.

Eventually I decided to play with some of my footy mates for the local junior cricket side. To do this I had to work out how I could protect myself. Mum introduced me for the first time to ladies' panty liners which I could put in my underwear. As I wasn't sure I was safe enough, I wore a second pair as extra protection. As much as I enjoyed playing, in the end I was just too paranoid about the soiling showing through the white pants so I retired (hurt!) at a very young age.

One of the great personal achievements   in my final year of school was to be chosen as both the summer and winter school sports captain. I was able to achieve this sporting recognition due to my parents and grandparents fierce wish to support me. They were always there to watch me play, to participate and to encourage me. I have no doubt that sport helped me feel accepted as a normal kid. The friendships I started then I retain and they will be mates for life.

My passion for the North Melbourne Football Club was getting even greater as I got older. It had played an incredibly important part of my family as generations of Ryan's supported the club. When I was seven-years of age, my dad had become officially involved as the club's weights coach during the club training sessions and eventually as trainer on match day.

Brad and I were therefore incredibly fortunate to grow up around the clubrooms and could see our heroes firsthand. Consequently some of the players and their wives became very close friends of my parents. For me NMFC was such an important part of my life, and it was a wonderful outlet for me especially when I was going through

The Head Master,
Waverley High School,
Waverley Road,
CHADSTONE, 3148.

Dear Sir,

Re: Gregory RYAN, Form 2, d.o.b. 9.5.64,
4 Ivydene Court, CHADSTONE, 3148.

I am writing to you with knowledge of Mrs. Ryan about her son in the hope that it may help Gregory if problems develop.

Gregory was admitted to the Children's Hospital on the day of his birth with an imperforate anus. He had a colostomy performed for this and ultimately he had a pull through operation done in December of 1965.

The normal child has three muscles controlling the anus, the internal sphincter, the external sphincter and the pubo-rectalis. Gregory was born without an internal sphincter and without an external sphincter, and the pubo-rectalis muscle had to be operated upon so as to allow the bowel to go through it. As you might expect, this makes the muscle system very much weaker than in the average child.

In addition, the bowel in this condition tends to be very sluggish, and Gregory is no exception. This means that he is very much more prone to constipation than the average child, and not only that, partly as the result of his original problem, and partly as a result of the operation, he is much less sensitive in the area, being relatively numb, and therefore unappreciative when there is bowel action in his rectum.

This makes it very much more difficult for these children to have satisfactory bowel control, and many of the children require frequent enemas to prevent them becoming loaded with faeces and soiling all the time.

Gregory in addition has had operations on both his testicles, and, when he was young he had a weakness in his bladder that allowed the urine to reflux back up to the kidneys. Ultimately, he seems to have outgrown this, and I don't think there is any likelihood of urine problems developing now.

......2

38

difficult times. The Club was also destined to play an important role in my later decline and recovery.

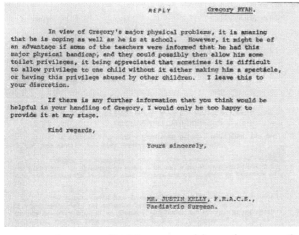 In March of 1977 I had an appointment with my RCH specialist Mr. Kelly and mum must have discussed with him that my school should be made fully aware of my medical issues and he subsequently wrote a letter to my School Principal dated 28th March 1977.

I look back now and wonder why it took the school and doctors 15 months to discuss my IA issues. I also wonder how many other kids still face the isolation and loneliness of bearing such secrets.

Even though the letter was sent to the high school principal, I have no recollection of my teachers actually extending me any particular support or toilet privileges.

There were no special need school assistants at that time and the brutal reality was that every day I was treated the same as any other kid. It was just sad that kids like me were expected to manage such highly complex issues. I wonder now whether this was a help or a hindrance to my development. Equal treatment helped me to protect my secret but the emotional turmoil certainly took its toll on my confidence.

As adolescence hit I was becoming more aware that I was indeed dramatically different to other kids and I started to ask more questions of my Doctors. In 1977, when I was 12 years old, I had my annual appointment with Dr. Kelly and I asked him to give me a better insight into issues.

He then proceeded to draw diagrams to show the difference between me and normal kids. This was the first time where I was

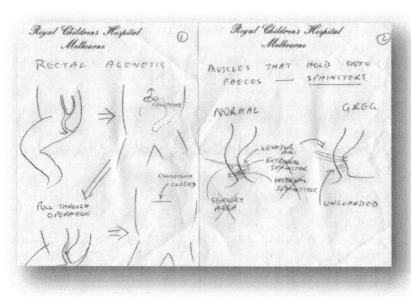

shown how I was different. I remember feeling that the decision to keep my secret was completely vindicated.

While generally I was a good student and didn't have any serious trouble, I was disruptive in class at times when I knew my bowels were playing up. I would   play the class clown so the teacher would remove me from that class. That was my strategy to protect myself in case I had an accident or was suffering bad flatulence. I couldn't tell anyone why I would behave that way, especially my teachers or my classmates. I didn't mind playing the class clown as I wanted others to laugh at me, believing that their laughter meant then they wouldn't tease me or expose my secret.

Of course, I would also spend more time in sick bay than other kids. The sick bay was my refuge, it made me feel safe away from the suspicious eyes of others. To be able to sustain the level of attendance I did was a great testimony to my parents.

As much as I tried to be normal I seemed always to be used as a side show when there were student doctors or other doctors visiting. My doctors seemed to enjoy showing me off as a rarity. As soon as I walked into a consulting room and there was a student doctor there I knew I would inevitably have to expose my bottom and genitals. As much as I hated it, I couldn't say no to my doctors. I knew they were trying to educate students and, if that meant exposing me to the examination, so be it.   As I got older the examinations became more intrusive but by then I had become conditioned to this process.

I was very naïve when it came to girls as well and suffered a very embarrassing incident when I was 15 years old on a school camp to the snow. It was the second night and after enjoying a fun day skiing all day, I had to hold on from going to the toilet so I didn't miss   any of the fun. But it came at a cost, as that night I was having a lot of difficulty going to the toilet and the entire group was going out for dinner.

As I was sitting there contemplating how I was going to approach the subject with the teachers, one of the girls came up to the senior lady teacher and said she was feeling unwell and that she didn't feel like going out. The teacher accepted the request and I saw that this was the chance I needed. I went to the teacher and asked if I could talk to her privately and admitted I was also feeling unwell. I suggested that I must have what the girl has and the teacher gave me an incredulous look and replied: "I doubt that very much. She is suffering from a girl's only issue, Greg."

The teacher allowed that I could also stay back at the lodge but the damage had been done and I was shattered and embarrassed. Not only was I battling going to the toilet at the time, I now felt like the teacher thought that I was very strange and weak.

All I could think of that night was that the teacher and others would be making fun of me and that my secret may be widely revealed. Thankfully, I heard no more.

Once I was in my mid-teenage years all my mates started to turn their attention to girls, but I was petrified by the possibility of a girlfriend discovering my secret. There is no way I thought that any girl would want to be around me because of my IA and genital issues, so I didn't even consider a loving relationship. Instead I developed great friendships with girls because I felt safer around them. Now I became everyone's friend. I could protect myself by being no competition to anyone.

My school reports always indicated that I was capable but emphasised that I needed to settle in class if my grades were to improve. By the end of 1980 my life was changed dramatically when I was advised by my school that I wouldn't be elevated to a final year 12. They suggested that I didn't meet requisite standards and that it was best that I left school and found a job.

I hadn't contemplated a career choice because I knew I had become addicted to the strange security of school. I had managed in my own way for six years and even though I wasn't anywhere near an A-Grade student.

I knew for me to have survived at school was worth so much more than any teachers report card could ever match. I might have not lived up to expectations as a student but I knew in my own heart and mind that I had succeeded in a normal world even though I was so different in so many ways.

There was a sense of sadness as well, even though I had got to the end of my school years I couldn't share with anyone else how really proud I was.

To others I may have been seen as a failure as I had not completed my year 12 level and achieved the Higher School Certificate. For me however, leaving school without my secret being exposed was my greatest achievement. The one subject at school that I had excelled at was *Keeping Secrets 101*, and if I was judging myself I would have proudly given myself an A+ grade.

I had survived primary & high school and now had no choice but to move out into the adult world where I would obviously be facing a whole new set of challenges.

Chapter 5 - Finding My Way

At the age of 17 years and 7 months I confronted the reality that my school days had ended. For me it was all about day by day survival at school, so I hadn't given a thought to what I wanted to do in the workforce. The one thing I did know however was that I had to have a career as a white-collar worker where I had easy access to a toilet. I needed an office environment, not a male dominated trades environment where I would feel especially vulnerable. I knew that protecting my secret by wearing a jumper around my waist would not be rational in the workplace. Time had caught up with me and my pride in getting through school without being exposed was now overridden by the fear of the unknown adult world.

When I met with my Career Advisor the reality hit that I had limited opportunities due to my school qualifications and my disability. I obviously wouldn't confide the latter with my advisor but it became clear to me that working in the banking industry could be suitable. I discussed this with my parents and as they were very supportive within a week I had applied for a position as a Junior Bank Clerk at the ANZ Bank. I made the decision not to mention my IA condition. As no one could see the massive scar on my stomach I just hoped I could "fake it to make it" as I had done all my life.

Within a week, I had received a letter from the ANZ Bank advising that I had a job interview.

I was incredibly apprehensive but I thought I handled the interview well and left thinking that the role would suit me. Two days later I got a phone call from the HR Manager and was told I had been successful. I was to start on a three-month probation period and then, if successful in this phase, I would continue on a full-time basis.

As I put down the phone I could see that mum was excited and dad proud. I was moved to see the emotion on mum's face as we both buried how difficult life had been for us to that time. As I was now entering the workforce, I hoped I could repay them through my achievements and attitudes.

The transition from boy to man was almost complete. I wasn't sure I was ready for it, and I had no idea how I would cope but this was now my life. Over the weeks prior to starting I had to come to grips with how I would be able to sustain my secret in the workplace. The one saving grace was that I had to be professionally dressed. Therefore, I could wear trousers that were very dark.

I discussed with Dr. Dammery how I was going to deal with the soiling issue. Our solution was for me to wear two pairs of underwear with enough folded toilet paper inserted in the first pair against my skin to absorb the leakage that might occur.

The hardest issue I was going to face was when I had to contend regularly with was the fecal incontinence issue of a "sneaky" hard piece of stool, which would appear in my rectum without warning.

As I had no sense of feeling at all in that area until it emerged, it really sent me into a panic. Once it occurred I would then have to clench my buttocks to retain it and then had to find a toilet immediately to pass the small motion.

There was also an ongoing issue with flatulence. Even though Mr. Kelly had told me early in my teenage years that I should not hold it in, as it was harmful, I had defied his direction. I learnt to control it as much as I could no matter the pain and discomfort it caused in a social, sporting and now a working environment. I perfected being able to practically run away from people when I had no option other than to release gas.

The first few months were difficult as I adapted to working in a professional environment and negotiating public transport. I experienced many difficult days with my bowels but always tried to show no emotion. I had to change my toilet paper protection many times but, gradually, I gained confidence.

My new regimen of protection was working and that made me feel less anxious but it also presented an issue that was unforeseen. It was very uncomfortable around my crotch area, since I was now wearing two pairs of underwear and had to ensure they were tight to keep the toilet paper inserted in correct place. I was now experiencing discomfort from the front as well as the back!

I continued to play competitive football with my mates as we moved from our junior club to a different league and I prolonged the use of rubbing dirt on my shorts each game day. I felt safe and they treated me as just one of the boys and that solidarity meant more to me that they could ever know.

It also had become totally evident to me by this age that I was different to my mates, in that I had no interest at all in alcohol or cigarettes. My mates were all beer drinkers and smokers and were always at me to have a try. I once tried a sip of beer just to get them off my back, but I ensured that I had a glass of Raspberry Lemonade close by. In front of a group at the Notting Hill Hotel I tentatively lifted the glass to my mouth to enthusiastic cheering from them all. I bought the glass to my mouth and took the smallest sip I could take and immediately spat it back out into the glass without even swallowing and grabbed the Raspberry Lemonade. All the mates booed in chorus but I declared that would be the last time they would see me drink a beer, and I've lived my life as a non-drinker since!

What of course the lads didn't understand was that I had a critically important reason why I would not drink alcohol. I needed to feel safe and I had to manage myself to guarantee that I had the safety of a toilet close by.

The one thing which did annoy me however was that ever since we had all turned 18, the boys and their partners in summer would go on weekend camping trips. The trips became legendary amongst our circle of mates, but I wasn't able to go with them. As there weren't easily accessible toilet facilities, there was no way I would put myself in such a predicament. It didn't matter at all to everyone else as, they would just make do in whatever way they could but this was a non-negotiable for me and I had to stay home.

In early 1983, we had graduated from underage football to playing against men in a senior competition. I had done my best not to let my IA affect my playing and had played over 100 games and in my U/16 year I was selected to play in a league representative team, which now seems pretty amazing given my physical issues.

I went along to the open age training that first week with great expectations. As my mates and I were getting ready to leave change rooms after training the Coach asked all the new boys to come with him. He got us together and announced, "Ok boys, you are all adults now playing with men, so you have to act like men. That means after training you just don't get your bags and go, you must have a shower with all the boys. We are all in this together, so there are no exceptions."

Everyone else nodded and expressed no issue but of course I had major concerns. I felt that feeling which I had experienced so many times before and I froze in fear. For me it was something that I could not even contemplate, as there was no way known I would reveal myself to any other person other than a doctor or nurse. To me it would mean the ultimate shame and embarrassment if I were to be exposed.

I didn't have the shower as the coach had requested but grabbed my bag, walked to my car and drove home. Within five minutes of leaving the ground and getting home, I knew I would never play football again! I spoke to my parents, told them I'd rather just go watch North play every week and that was that, my much-loved football career was over!

Somewhere in this time I convinced myself I wasn't a real man and this belief became embedded in my psyche. All I had ever wanted was to be accepted as normal but there was a daily, stark reminder that my normal was different and there was no way to change my anatomy.

Chapter 6 –Normalisation

Despite my doubts and some tense moments, I lasted at the ANZ Bank for three years before I changed jobs and began work in an office environment at Budget-Rent-A-Car. As dad had a connection with the executive managers of Budget through the NMFC gymnasium he alerted me to a job opportunity. I applied and was successful in getting the position.

I hadn't felt comfortable working in a front office environment as a bank teller and serving customers for the majority of the day. I was always on the alert regarding my IA issue, be it the paranoia of someone seeing my soiling patch, or involuntary flatulence or having a "sneaky stool" appear.

As I had no feeling at all that a stool may be in my rectum, the only "signal", I have to use my bowels is the pain or cramps I get in my stomach due to the laxatives I was taking, which adds to the fear of the unknown. The "sneaky stool" would only become apparent when it is too late and I feel against my skin around my opening.

I couldn't feel comfortable and was always on alert and I'm sure this was reflected in my work performance and productivity.

I immediately felt comfortable working at Budget in their main office in North Melbourne. It suited me perfectly. I was working in an office environment and I could deal with the issues relating to my IA a lot better than when working at the bank. I was no longer under the constant appraisal of customers. I could now sit at a desk with my fellow workers and come and go as I pleased. An added sense of security was the knowledge that my grandparents only lived five minutes from the ground.

In April 1984 as a 20-year-old, mum and I went to our yearly appointment with Mr. Kelly at RCH and it was agreed by all, that I was now too old for the RCH and that Dr. Dammery would take over my medical needs. It became apparent that there was no consideration for a transition from Mr. Kelly and RCH. However, I knew I was extremely fortunate that at least I had Dr. Dammery. I trusted him implicitly, but I did feel a sense of abandonment regarding the safety net that I desperately needed.

Nevertheless, my life was good and I was going out with my mates and enjoying being one of the boys. To everyone I was as normal as they were. My non-drinking had its benefits for them as they knew they had a designated driver. They understood that when I started to jingle my car keys it was time for last drinks as I would be heading for home very shortly.

When our whole crew was at a nightclub, the boys would just congregate and drink while their girlfriends would want to dance. Since I loved to dance, this engaged me joyfully. I became the pseudo-boyfriend for many of the girls on the dance floor and that suited the lads. I did have some issues regarding my IA at times, but I found I could generally adapt without anyone realizing.

Sadly, there was one incident that haunts me still. We were at our regular nightclub and I was on the dance floor with one of the girlfriends and we were dancing enthusiastically, when suddenly I felt something rub against my lower leg, inside my pants. I immediately knew what had happened, the toilet paper that I had folded in my underpants had somehow slipped and had fallen down my pants. I tried to maintain composure and get to the toilet paper before it fell.

Horrifyingly within ten seconds it had fallen on to the dance floor. I immediately bent, as if I was doing up my shoe laces, grabbed the stained toilet paper and hurriedly put it in my pocket. I was convinced every person on the dance floor had seen what happened, especially my dance partner. As soon as the song stopped, I indicated to her I was going back to the crew and we walked off. I informed her I was going to the toilet and when I reached that sanctuary I can remember disposing of the paper and sitting there shaking and feeling as I had in the early days of primary school. I was petrified by fear.

I composed myself and returned to the others telling them I wasn't feeling well and was going home. Once I got to my car I sat and couldn't stop the emotions flowing out as tears. I was convinced that my secret was now blown. After an agonizing night, I woke on the Saturday morning convinced that all would know the darkest truths. To my overwhelming relief when I met everyone again that night, it wasn't mentioned.

As the early days of working passed I was accruing some funds and a friend of mine told me of an exciting cruise experience she had enjoyed. So, with a burst of poise I decided to try one myself. Of course, I went on my own because of my exposure concerns.

I went on the cruise and I enjoyed myself, finding it suited me

well. If I had any bowel issues I wasn't more than a few minutes away from my cabin and my sanctuary: the toilet.

This initial tourist activity of mine was to later have far reaching influences.

Chapter 7 – Here we go again

Since the day I was born, the major focus of my medical attention has logically been my IA condition. As I have aged, I have found that the penile abnormality and undescended testes have caused me more embarrassment and psychological pain.

As my medical records show, the journey through my urological issues has been torturous. These comments seem to suggest that there are medical reasons why I was born with issues relating to my genitals and exhaustive research underlines that there is a definite correlation between males born with IA and simultaneous genital and urological issues. This helps me justify that I am not as much a freak as I have believed but sadly it doesn't change how I look physically or how I feel emotionally.

I have had to endure many instances of pain and discomfort with my penis and testes since birth, and when I refer to these medical records it just confirms   why I struggle both emotionally and physically. As I got older I found the issues I had were now becoming more to the forefront in my mind and they have affected my self-esteem greatly.

I had been out on a Saturday night like most 22-year-olds and arrived home around midnight and went to bed. I woke up around 2.30am with a pain in my lower stomach but it wasn't like a normal bowel pain: I felt nauseous and knew something wasn't right. I went to the toilet, but nothing happened and I went back to bed hoping that it was just a cramp. Within a half hour the pain was more intense, and I felt like I had been hit in the testicles. The pain became so severe that I woke my parents and told them yet again that I needed to go to hospital.

I arrived at the Emergency Ward of the Moorabbin Hospital around 3.00am and was examined by doctors who advised us that I had a condition called "torsion of the testes". It meant that somehow both testicles had become twisted and I required emergency surgery. I was advised that this condition could be fatal if not immediately corrected. As I lay there awaiting the surgeon to arrive, I could feel the resentment building. Yet another physical crisis! Why me?

I was transferred to a ward awaiting the preparations for my surgery and agitated unsuccessfully to get the hospital to call Dr. Dammery. I was desperate for his re-assurance. Once the surgeon, Dr. Derek Richmond, arrived and spoke to mum I settled as mum gave Dr. Richmond details of my history regarding my IA and testes. Dr. Richmond explained that he found it very rare that he would see a case of Torsion Testes when undescended testes surgery had been conducted.

It wasn't the first time a Doctor thought I was rare and it wasn't to be the last either. At about 5.00am I was wheeled in to another operating theatre for more surgery. By the time surgery was complete I had two more scars to add to my collection but at least these two were well and truly hidden from view. Dr. Dammery made a special trip to see me in the hospital that afternoon.

I spent four days in hospital recovering from the surgery and it took me three days before I could even attempt to walk, and that was very bow-legged. I was advised to take two weeks' sick leave to recover from surgery and spent that time having salt baths to assist recovery of the wounds and laying with my legs up so not to put any extra pressure on the area.

With this latest surgery came different challenges for me at an emotional level. I would require two weeks' sick leave, and had to advise my boss what had happened. I could see he was trying not to laugh at the sensitive nature of the operation. While I also saw the funny side his smirk just added credibility to my tactic of keeping my IA condition secret. I later found that workplace confidentiality was not protected. When I had returned to work, all staff seemed to know the nature of my surgery. My severe low self-esteem due to my IA and genital self-consciousness deepened and I felt even more outcast.

About six months after the surgery the pain returned in my right testicle. Dr. Dammery diagnosed me with a case of Epididymitis: another new word to add to my extensive list of medical terms. The inflammation of the epididymis tube was very painful, and he advised the cause was probably related to the surgery. The course of antibiotics eased the pain and inflammation, but I was becoming increasingly frustrated with the chronic pain so Dr. Dammery organized another appointment with Dr. Richmond.

Dr. Richmond examined both testes and he immediately identified how tender I was in the right testicle. He noted that it was definitely sitting higher than the left and that the tenderness wasn't normal. He also declared that the issues with my Imperforate Anus, penis, testes, and bladder etc. could explain why my recovery after surgery was not smooth. Normally, he assured me, his patients would recover well and have no issues going forward.

By this stage I was in my early 20's and still hadn't had a serious girlfriend. I had lost all confidence with the recurring issues happening below my waist. As much as I tried to adapt and adjust over the months following Dr. Richmond's appointment, I continued to feel something still was not right with my testicle. Dr. Dammery agreed that 12 months of antibiotics were not assisting the tenderness. So, we booked a time with the local Radiology centre for a fresh examination. I didn't ask what I was getting done; I just assumed it was some sort of X-Ray. Little did I know that I was about to suffer the most intriguing investigation of my life.

The regular intrusions in regards examinations of my anus, penis & testes could not prepare me for what I had to face in this radiology centre. I was shocked when a young female nurse walked in and asked me to lie down with my legs spread over the bed. She explained that she was responsible for giving me an ultrasound on my testicles. Over the next 30 minutes I was examined and re-examined and examined again by the young nurse, a senior nurse and the radiographer. They eventually decided that the strange ultrasound images were showing that my right testicle was upside down and causing my extreme discomfort.

I felt vindicated because I knew that something had been wrong with my body. The radiology team confirmed that they hadn't seen anything like it. However, I left their feeling confused, grateful that there was nothing serious found, but left wondering if once again I would have to face more surgery.

When I next walked into Dr. Dammery's rooms he looked at me with a wry smile as he had already received the radiology report and not for the first time reminded me that I was one of his most interesting patients. But it was now back to Dr. Richmond. Dr. Richmond asked if I could live with the discomfort rather than taking the risk of further surgery. He was reluctant to undertake more surgery due to my history. He advised that he like a second opinion and was sending me to see a Dr. Collins, who was a urology specialist at the Epworth Hospital, before deciding a next step.

I couldn't secure an appointment with Dr. Collins for two months and in the interim I did not wear anything too tight as my right testicle was not sitting in correct position and any extra pressure added to the discomfort. When I eventually met with him, I handed Dr. Collins my referral letter and the accompanying radiology pictures and report. I wasn't surprised when he agreed that he was also perplexed as to how this has happened after my torsion surgery.

After the inevitable painful examination, Dr. Collins advised that unfortunately his counsel was that I must contend with this discomfort, and adjust to the pain as part of my daily life. Ironically, he asked why I was wearing two sets of underwear and I explained my soiling protection method. Immediately he strongly recommended that I try to wear looser fitting underwear as it might ease the pressure on my right testes. I had walked into his office hoping that he could give me answers regarding my testes now I was walking out with no solution to either of my disabilities. Later at home I discussed with mum and dad and we agreed to go with the doctor's suggestions knowing that if it got worse there was always the last resort of the surgery.

Mum's suggestion regarding my underwear was that I   wear boxer shorts and use normal sized ladies' panty-liners as I had when I played cricket many years before. I always felt more secure and safe with the folded toilet paper in between the two pair of underpants and was reluctant to even contemplate changing my regime. Despite the impending embarrassment, I decided to give it a go and on the weekend mum and I went shopping for shorts and liners.

I went to work on the Monday feeling very nervous as I was trialing my new regime of wearing only one pair of boxer shorts with the "Winged Panty Liner" stuck to them and then the normal panty liner placed on top of that one. (But I did take some spare sets of underpants with me just in case.)

If I wasn't insecure enough when it came to someone seeing me with my pants down, this heaped up the potential humiliation. I imagined my peers seeing me wearing a female hygiene product and I still live with that morbid fear.

Of course the change created new issues. With my right testicle now being more free I found that it would get into uncomfortable positions and I would seemingly forever have to adjust myself.

That has become a source of embarassment over the years and I have even had two female friends ask me why I touched myself so much. I had always tried to do it in private and in a manner where I thought no one would notice but unfortunately I didn't succeed.

I also have had to constantly adjust myself at the back of my pants to ensure the panty liner is lined correctly with my anal area so any soiling was being captured. I did have a female workmate ask me to "stop playing with your bum" and that heightened my paranoia. I shudder when I think of how many people over the years have noticed me doing this and what they thought of me.

My adjustments occur countless times a day and that is the price I (and any observers) pay for me feeling physically comfortable and emotionally safe.

Unfortunately the list of physical problems was about to have a new item added. Because of always straining when emptying my bowels the added pressure on my prostate gland initiated an involuntary fluid discharge through my penis. When it first occured I was shocked believing something was desperately wrong. Dr. Dammery advised that I had developed Chronic Prostatitis. I was beginning to learn that chronic means continuing......and that became my experience.

Chapter 8 – Finding Love

A few months later I decided to do another cruise, which was to be significantly different because I met a girl and we spent a lot of time together. I had still not had a serious relationship and after the recent issue I had with my testes, my self-esteem was even lower than normal. At the halfway of the cruise I was introduced to one of the girls and miraculously we danced together exclusively, and I enjoyed an amazing sense of intimacy.

Later we arranged to catch up again and we subsequently became inseparable for the remaining five days of the cruise. When the cruise finished, and we had to say goodbye it was very emotional for both of us. At 22 I had at last felt the joys of romantic love. She accepted me and my bundle of insecurities and for the next few months we regularly flew interstate to see each other but the distance eventually made our relationship unsustainable. Nevertheless, that cruise and the exciting woman who opened my soul and gave me some confidence will always have a very special place in my heart.

By early 1987, I changed jobs again, even though I had loved my three and a half years at Budget, I had been transferred out of the leasing section and hadn't felt comfortable in the new department. I made the decision to move on and enrolled in a couple of job agencies to take on casual employment for the imminent future.

I worked casually for six months and spent most of this time working in a small office in the city with American Express. This involved dealing with big organizations and I struck up a friendship with some people at Westpac Banks Consumer Finance Centre and they advised me that a full-time position had become available there. I applied and was successful. Even though I had worked in the ANZ Bank when I first left school, this was a totally different role and one I knew would suit me as it was in a back-office environment with no direct customer contact.

I worked at the Consumer Finance Centre for two and a half years and in that time, saw my department diminish from four people to one over the twelve months. My role meant visiting branch and local District Operation Centre's (DOC's) to conduct training sessions. Once again, due to being in a back-office environment I could deal with my IA issues and as always, I had Dr. Dammery to get me through if I had difficulties.

Much to my surprise a further job opportunity arose at a District Operation Centre responsible for all the back-office processing of each branch. What I didn't expect when I started working at the centre was that by transferring there my life would be changed forever.

The role required substantial contact with a key person at each branch. In my case I had one large branch and a smaller one for which I was responsible, and I had to work hand in hand with the Managers' assistant at each branch. With the larger branch, I had to spend a lot more time corresponding and talking to one of the girls. Over a few months, we became close by chatting constantly and it got to the stage where we were flirting with each other and becoming friends rather than colleagues. It became obvious that we were spending a lot of time on the phone together and we each copped good natured banter from our work mates.

Much to my initial shock and delight, that girl and I started a relationship in August 1990 and to the absolute surprise of my family and friends, within three months I had moved out of home and into a unit with her. Six months later I had proposed, she had accepted and soon after we had a big engagement party at my parents' house. I hadn't imagined ever getting married, as I was convinced I wouldn't be good enough for any woman given my physical health issues. I had assumed that I would have platonic relationships with females all my life. But my fiancée changed that, and helped me face a reality that I had not dared to face. I now had to face revealing my secret to her as my closest friend.

All my childhood, my parents or doctors where the ones who dictated who knew and who didn't, and it wasn't until I was around 12-years old that I declared that I didn't want anyone else to know. Now I was disclosing my secret in my own words, to the woman I loved. It was the hardest thing I had ever done. As I struggled through my explanations, my wife could see how hard it was for me and her empathy and understanding amazed me. I had inadvertently answered some of her confusions about why I spent so much time in the toilet and why I was paranoid about showering in front of her.

I explained that I still wanted to keep silent publicly and she respected my privacy which was immensely reassuring. I knew my secret was safe with her and I am overwhelmingly grateful for her integrity.

I asked a lifelong mate of mine Michael Baillie to be my best man and my brother Brad was a groomsman and we were married in February 1992 at the same church my parents were married in, St Mary's East St Kilda. The next day we travelled to Los Angeles and then Honolulu for our Honeymoon. By late 1993, we moved out of the unit and bought a house in Mulgrave, thanks to the generosity of my family. We were happy to be in the little world of our house.

I was now in a situation that I never expected and didn't think I deserved. I was a husband. With that came whole new challenges that I had tried to avoid all my adult life. I had been so self-centred about my IA issues and had to now learn the impact on my wife.

My bizarre eating habits were just one example that created significant tensions. Since I was a child I had learnt that I could only eat a very narrow range of foods without causing great grief to my bowels. I had learnt to refuse any new foods or change my diet. I had been fortunate that my mum and my grandparents would cook me the same basic meals and my body adjusted to this dietary regime.

Once my body allowed me to function on basic food and laxatives, I was totally focused of being risk averse. Consequently, I have never accepted an invitation to a dinner party in my life. I am too embarrassed to offend the host by not eating the meal they prepare. With either a work or sporting function, I would accompany my wife but I would eat beforehand. This caused great embarrassment and much evasive dialogue. It was also incredibly frustrating at home as my terribly restricted diet caused many issues for us.

More significant, and at a truly personal level, was my fear of real intimacy. I was never able to bring myself to discuss our physical links as I was tortured by shame and embarrassment. I had successfully kept these feelings and emotions hidden over the years by avoiding relationships. Now I was married I had to confront this reality but in fact I couldn't, and I didn't. I retreated into silence and let the frictions became a further mental burden for me. I had replaced one secret with another and shifted my pain on to the shoulders of the woman I loved.

The burden would eventually be intolerable for us both.

Chapter 9 - Moving Times

In mid-1994, I became aware of positions being advertised in the National Australia Bank Personal Credit Office and due to the salary offered I applied for a position. I was successful and was subsequently positioned at their Head Office in the city. Once again, the back-office role suited me well.

In early 1999, I had asked Dr. Dammery about further addressing my IA issue as my soiling was becoming heavier and more prevalent. There was an ongoing issue of dealing with my "nappy rash" due to increased mucous leakage causing an acidic reaction on the skin around my anal opening. As I had previously had appendix surgery performed by Professor Polglase we decided he was the perfect person to undertake the surgery. He indicated that he could assist me by doing corrective surgery trimming the excess mucous from my bowel lining. He also suggested that he could tighten my anus to assist in minimising the amount of leakage I was having daily. He warned me however that he couldn't guarantee success due to all the scar tissue caused by the numerous intrusive surgical procedures I had experienced.

The surgery was scheduled as a day procedure but while lying on the operating table waiting to be anaesthetised, I had a flashback to my childhood and I unexpectedly began to cry. When the professor approached, he noticed my sobbing, but I assured him that I wanted the surgery to go on. The next thing I knew, I was woken by a nurse in the post operation room. I immediately felt that I had a very large pad around my anus but no pain. The professor came to see me and first considered my emotions. I said I was fine and apologised to him for my humiliating crying outburst. He was supportive and pleased with the surgery but expected that I would be in pain once the medication had worn off. He warned that I might bleed heavily for a few days and he prescribed a heavy laxative. I was thankful for that because I was already feeling anxious about getting constipated and my fears of another rectal enema.

My wife collected me and fortunately I had two weeks' sick leave to get over the surgery. I was shocked that I was bleeding as much as I was and I required salt baths twice a day to ease the pain of the rash that had begun again.

When I went back to work, I was not fully recovered but I had little choice, as at that stage I was a team leader and felt an obligation to my staff. The worst part of returning was that I had to have a blown-up ring to sit on to alleviate pressure on my bottom. I told people my surgery was to remove some haemorrhoids, which caused mirth and a lot of stirring. I was happy to accept that as alternative to exposing the real issue.

In mid-1999 management announced that the Department had been awarded a Best of the Best award from the NAB board. To celebrate this award there was to be a Black-Tie Celebration where 30 staff members were selected to receive individual awards for their work performance. There were over 300 staff members working at the PCO at that stage and I was fortunate to be one of the staff members selected to receive an award. It was very pleasing to be recognised in such a way and was wonderful to enjoy the night with my wife who was recognised the year before in a similar way. I still have the trophy I received that night with the engraving:

GREG RYAN
BEST OF THE BEST
IN OPERATIONS EXCELLENCE 1999

proudly displayed. Somewhere deep inside me this award and my earlier football success were important in helping me balance some of the physical and mental torments that had plagued me.

In late-1999, NAB announced they had purchased a USA based banking company called HomeSide Lending. It specialised in the bank lending area and was going to be responsible for the back-office assistance in processing documentation to all NAB branches, starting mid-2000. With my experience as a Supervisor in the frenetic environment of Mortgage Discharge and Settlements Department of the NAB, the opportunity for me to apply as a Team Leader at HomeSide came about.

I discussed the opportunity with my wife and she was very encouraging. With my previous experience, I was always strangely confident that I was in with a chance and was subsequently offered the position and the substantial pay rise. I hadn't previously been ambitious in any job I had held. I was just content to do my job to the best of my ability. I had the same attitude to work as I had at school: my priority always being to keep my secret intact.

I started my new role in January 2000 and spent the first few months learning the computer codes and procedures. I was confident with my knowledge of the legal discharge procedures involving other banks, solicitors and conveyancers, but to learn brand new procedures was challenging. I had a staff of more than 20 people with this new role and was finding my feet as leader of that group. However, I made an appointment with Dr. Dammery in the middle period of 2000 as I was starting to feel a sense of vulnerability that was affecting my performance. The unexplained vulnerability was unnerving and while Dr. Dammery was incredibly supportive we couldn't find a meaningful explanation.

In August, my wife and I decided we needed a holiday just to have some time to ourselves, so we booked a trip to Port Douglas for the second week of October. It was exactly what we needed as the year so far had been very intense for us both. We boarded the plane looking forward to having an enjoyable time together and for the first three days we were having exactly that. We had been on tours on each day and we happily had booked a tour to the Great Barrier Reef on the fourth day.

At 6.00am of the morning of that tour my mobile phone rang. It was mum. From her voice, I immediately knew something was dreadfully wrong. I learned that my beloved grandfather Tom had died. Fortunately, he had passed gently in his sleep next to Nan but she, my mum and my dad were obviously deeply upset. I told them we would be on the first flight. As soon as I got off the phone my wife and I broke down in each other's arms.

The next two or three hours were a blur as we organised the flight and transport from the Cairns airport. When we got to Nan's, I had to do one of the hardest things I ever had done in my life. I had to walk down the passage as I had done thousands of times before, but this time Tom was not there to greet me.

Selfishly, I was quietly thankful that I hadn't been there to see Tom's body taken away. Tom had meant so much to me and the next week was lived in a mist as we struggled through the funeral and began coming to terms with the fact that Tom had gone forever.

In the sad, reflective moments, amidst too many tears and the laughter of Tom's admiring and loving friends and family, my life was changing significantly, but not in a way that I had ever expected.

Chapter 10 - Things Fall Apart

The first time I felt there was something really not quite right with me emotionally was in early February 2001. I was feeling low, tired, and didn't want to be at work and didn't want to be at home with my wife either. I just wanted to feel invisible.

During one lunch break I had cause to travel into the city centre. Instead of doing the energetic thing of walking the one kilometre as I would have done normally I decided instead to take the lazy option of catching a tram. On this five-minute tram ride I succumbed to a terror and burst into tears. It was at that moment that I recognized that while I had had numerous issues with my health since birth, most had clear physical causes. Now there were no physical signs of something being wrong, I didn't need to find a toilet urgently; I didn't need a Band-Aid; I didn't have a headache; I was simply scared and confused.

I composed myself and went about what I had to do in the city then walked back to work and   called Dr. Dammery for an urgent appointment. To my disappointment, he was on leave and wouldn't be back for two weeks. I made the appointment for the day he was returning and hoped that I could cope until then.

For the next two weeks, I went about my life with a lethargy and laziness I had not felt before. I could not confront any issues that required decisiveness. I didn't tell my wife what happened on the tram or what I was going through. The accumulated pressures were of course pushing us more and more apart.

While I was at work, I would do anything possible to avoid making any decision. My job had become highly-pressured and operating in what had become a hostile working environment was eroding me. Gone were the days where I could run on adrenaline and answer each enquiry with the utmost confidence. I was second guessing my own decisions and asking my staff to make their inquiries of another Team Leader. I made my desk a cocoon. I had become a hermit in the thriving bank's workplace.

I told my wife that I had booked the appointment with Dr. Dammery as a check-up regarding my anus. She accepted my explanation. Ever since corrective surgery performed by Professor Polglase just over 12 months earlier, she knew I was having more troubles, but we had lost the ability to discuss my disabilities. I felt bad that I had lied to her after all the things she had endured alongside me. I had not revealed how bad things at work had become.

I got to Dr. Dammery's rooms and immediately felt safe. I told him I had become stressed and fearful at work and lost total confidence. I had become withdrawn and felt I was letting my staff and myself down. I also talked to him about my failures at home and he acknowledged that he had intuited that things had not been going well. As we talked my emotions exploded and I again began to cry uncontrollably. Dr. Dammery advised that he would refer me to a Psychiatrist (Dr. Fred Hocking) and confirmed that I should make an urgent appointment. He believed I was demonstrating the symptoms of chronic depression.

He explained that the human spirit was like a glass that can overflow as you lose control and my glass was well and truly overflowing. Dr. Dammery described how my medical issues and my personal and work issues were compounding. I went home and confided in my wife. We both knew that we faced an uncertain future.

After a sleepless night, I went into work feeling so anxious that during our normal Team Leaders meeting I suddenly dissolved and started to weep. I was completely embarrassed and humiliated. My boss discreetly and generously arranged that the other Team Leaders leave. On hearing my explanation, he recommended that I should go home immediately.

My wife and mum and dad met me at home and we desperately discussed the meaning and impact of chronic depression on our futures. Thanks to Dr. Dammery, I could organize an appointment with Dr. Hocking for the next day at 10.00am. This gave us all some calm and hope.

I woke up early the next morning and drove to my 10.00am appointment with Dr. Hocking at his Albert Park rooms not knowing what to expect. I attended alone even though my wife was quite prepared to come with me. I wasn't sure what to anticipate so I wanted to go alone. My pre-conceived perception of psychiatrists was drawn from what I had seen on television. I had no idea what they did: was I going to be asked to lie down on a couch? Was I going to be hypnotized? I had no idea at all, but the one thing that I did know is that if Dr. Dammery recommended him, I knew that Dr. Hocking would be the best person to help me.

At 10.00am exactly, an elderly man came into the Waiting Room and softly called my name. Dr. Hocking shook my hand in a gentle and reassuring way and immediately I felt at ease. The next hour was to be one of the most defining of my life. I talked about my intense work pressures; the death of my beloved grandfather; the complexity of my marriage; and the daily issues linked to my bowel condition. Thankfully Dr. Hocking was aware of Imperforate Anus and he ratified that this had played an enormous part in shaping my emotional life.

Dr. Hocking advised that I had suffered a nervous breakdown, which I found incredibly confronting. He arranged that I take sick leave for the next two and a half weeks and prescribed a course of anti-depressants. I left my first appointment feeling totally exhausted and drained but relieved that I had some understanding to what was happening to me.

I called my wife as soon as I got home, and she was relieved that I sounded better. Deep down I knew our marriage was in serious trouble, but I ignored that reality as much as possible as I tried to concentrate on getting myself stronger. Once she joined me at an appointment with Dr. Hocking but couldn't really understand what I was going through. I accepted and appreciated her confusion as well as her magnificent support.

My work was very understanding when I explained to them that I needed to take two and a half weeks off due to illness. I was very reluctant for anyone other than my manager and team leaders to be made aware of the reason for my absence, as I was totally embarrassed. At that time, I was under the impression that after rest, medication and appointments with Dr. Hocking I would be ready to re-commence my work commitments. Sadly, depression is not so easy to beat.

As I talked to Dr. Hocking I realized that I had not effectively grieved or accepted the death of my beloved grandfather Tom. My family reinforced the doctor's analysis explaining how I not once spoken about Tom's death instead avoiding the reality by describing his dying as "the Tom business". This was another issue that I had been submerging rather than confronting. Unfortunately, the cloud of sadness and anxiety continued to hang over me.

After the time off work and five appointments with Dr. Hocking we agreed that I would go back to work. I walked in feeling energized. After meeting with my boss and other team leaders, I was ready to give it my best shot. After an hour or so of passionate engagement however I felt a surge of terror rip through my body. An overwhelming feeling of anxiousness swept over me and I was shattered that my world was again falling apart.

I needed to hide so, terribly ironically it now seems, I walked quickly to the toilet and locked myself into a cubicle, bursting again into uncontrollable tears. How could I go back to my desk and face people? What was I going to say to my family? What was I going to say to my boss and work colleagues? In those ten minutes with so many things going through my head, the one thing that wasn't clouded in my mind was that it was abundantly clear that I was still desperately unwell.

The next few hours become a hectic haze as I confirmed my failure to my family and psychiatrist. My boss and workmates were equally dismayed and within an hour I was on the way home. The weight of the world felt on my shoulders and I suddenly knew that another episode in my life was ending and a dark door opening.

I might have thought that I had reached my lowest ebb from an emotional health point of view at that moment, but it was part of the rollercoaster which is depression. I was learning that the "black dog" was now mine to endure. I was admitted to the Ainslie Private Hospital and immediately felt safe, knowing that this was the right decision. The plan was

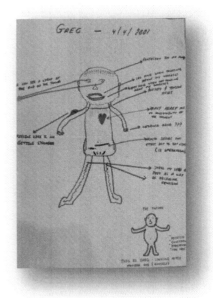

for me to stay only three or four days so I could have a break from my life.

I was admitted, shown to my private room and then waited for the resident Doctor, a Psychiatrist Dr. Lionel Chatz, who came to see me, and we chatted for an hour. He had been briefed by both Dr. Dammery and Dr. Hocking so that allayed any fears I had of being under the care of a different doctor.

I was only in there for a few hours when I met other patients and for the first time in a couple of months, I knew I wasn't alone. For the first time, I could see that there were others who understood what I was trying so hard to understand. I was dealing with my bowel issues daily without much thought which, on reflection, shows how much trouble I was in. Not in my wildest dreams would I have ever considered that my secret would play second fiddle to anything else in my life.

In the security of the therapy sessions I began to both understand, and claw my way back into some level of, emotional balance. This is a drawing on my third day in Ainslie Hospital in a Group therapy session, after being asked to express my feelings at that moment.

After three days, it was decided that I needed to stay longer. This suited me as I felt I was becoming stronger each day. On the eighth day, my wife made a surprise visit to see me early in the morning. She said that she had come to the realization that our marriage was over. Under the influence of my medication, and the false sense of strength drawn from this safe environment this seemed logical and the only realistic path for us. It is only now, as I write this, do I fully feel the gut-wrenching impact of my wife's very understandable reaction.

I discharged myself from the hospital three days later and went straight to a real estate agent and put our house on the market. Within a period of four months, I had lost my much-loved grandfather, had a nervous breakdown, became disassociated from my workplace, and faced the despair of a marital separation, moved out of my marital home as well as preparing it for market. Adding the burden of my daily health issues this body and mind of mine was on the verge of complete destruction. I am just so fortunate that I had an incredibly supportive family and the most amazing medicos in Dr. Hocking and Dr. Dammery who helped me survive the imperfect storm.

I rented an apartment in the city after our separation and I was desperate to get my own place and become well enough to return to work at the bank. I had to take extended sick leave and the bank kept me on full salary for which I was very grateful. I had thoughts of resigning, but thankfully Dr. Dammery & Dr. Hocking advised me to hold onto at least that one fixed point. They both were of the opinion the bank environment had contributed to my breakdown due to work pressures, but I blamed only myself.

After about a month of recuperation I felt I was capable of returning to work on light duties. Three days a week of filing was all I could manage but the emotion of office politics quickly ground me down. Smirks and backhanded comments about the supervisor laid low were too much to bear and shortly afterwards I dissolved again. Eventually I received notice that a component in the superannuation package of every NAB employee enabled me to receive a Temporary Disablement Benefit (TSB). I had no idea what this was, but I knew it was my only real option at the time. Because I met the criteria of not being able to sustain my working obligations due to medical issues, I received about 70% of salary.

Unfortunately, I had a severe relapse with my mental health at the end of July. I had begun to think of self-harm as my way of redressing all my failures. Thankfully my reliance on my doctor's advice meant that within a very short time I was re-admitted to Ainslie Private Hospital. Again, I had an overwhelming sense of safety within this sanctuary. I was there for four days and my ex-wife came to visit, which I really appreciated. It showed she still cared and was concerned for my well-being. I was, and am, pleased that there had been no animosity between us since our separation.

I had been in discussions with both Dr. Hocking and Dr. Dammery and they believed my prospects of returning to the NAB in any capacity were very doubtful and so advised the Trustees in their medical reports.

Two months later I was asked to attend an appointment with an independent doctor to determine whether I was entitled to a payout called a Partial Disablement Benefit. This was, in effect, an acknowledgement that I would be unable to return to the bank and resume my normal duties. I subsequently received further correspondence confirming that benefit.

To my overwhelming relief, the work tension was finally over. It had been approaching twelve months since I walked out of work in tears. I had always prided myself on my work ethic and now considered myself a total failure. I had received a financial settlement, but no amount of money could replace my damaged self-image.

But just as I was finally coming to grips with my new life situation in January 2002, I suffered a very traumatic issue with my physical health which was totally unexpected and was to lead to the scariest moment of my life. On this morning I tried to go to the toilet but was constipated and immediately feared having to have another rectal enema. I was fortunate that I had been able to avoid having an enema for many years by keeping to my strict dieting regime.   I went into a mild panic mode after I was unable to pass any motions.

As always when I had a failed attempt at the toilet I immediately took some extra laxatives in a hope that they would work within a few hours. I had spent nearly 30 minutes on the toilet and my legs and bottom were numb and I was soaking wet from perspiration. I then did what I have always done, and that was call mum to tell her what was happening.

My parents were holidaying at Rosebud (over an hour away) so I felt a sense of isolation and vulnerablity, but once again mum told me to settle down and just wait as the laxatives would take a while to take effect. I couldn't tell her about my concern with the discharge and penis pain I was experiencing as I hadn't discussed the issue of the chronic prostatitis with anyone other than Dr. Dammery. I was just too ashamed to discuss this with mum. (I even chose to hide it from my ex-wife for the whole eleven years we were together).

I got off the phone and tried to relax. I laid down for over an hour but then started to get pains in my bowel so, hoping the laxatives were starting to work, I decided to try again. For the next ten minutes, I strained as much as I could and ignored the penis discharge but then I looked down and I saw the discharge had turned blood red. I can't describe the feeling I had at that moment when I was realized that blood was now coming out of my penis.

I then drove myself in a panicked state to the Emergency Department of the Epworth Hospital and I endured one of the most chaotic and distressing afternoons of my life. I had the much-despised enema and the consolation of knowing that the blood was not symptomatic of cancer. I was relieved to learn that I had burst a blood vessel in the penis and that my straining had almost certainly caused this temporary distress. I would of course from this point on recognize that the fear that I felt was just around every corner of my IA journey.

Many years later, when I was discussing my urological issues with my psychiatrist, he reminded me that I had faced a unique congruence of events. Combining issues arising from my rare IA condition, genital abnormalities, countless surgeries and the bizarre upside-down testicle was challenge enough. Living through the social outcomes of these physical aberrations was another thing entirely.

Chapter 11 - Starting Over

The first thing I did for myself after the latest health scare and TSP confirmation and payout, was to arrange to move out of the rented city apartment. I went there in the first place to be close to work and once that failed, I was stuck there as I had signed a 12-month lease agreement. I hadn't enjoyed the living space for the last few months and started looking in the North Melbourne area, so I could be close to Nan and the North Melbourne Football ground.

I was fortunate that a small two-bedroom house almost immediately became available only a five-minute walk to Nan's, and only a two-minute drive to the footy ground. I had to pay extra to get out of my lease at the apartment, but at that time I couldn't have cared less. This was all about me moving forward with my life and shifting to this house felt the perfect way to start.

I was now in a position where I could concentrate on getting better with no external pressures. The one thing that had kept me half way sane over the previous few months was going to North Melbourne Football Club training two or three times each week. I could get out of the house from 3.30pm to 6.00pm and feel like a normal person.

One of the off-field icons of the Club, Judy Francis, was at training for each session preparing the before and after food for the players. My family and I had known Jude for years and we had always got on well. Jude was aware of my health battles and was also incredibly supportive. She encouraged me to come to the Club and sit in the room where she prepared the food. Her generosity helped provide me with the refuge I so craved and needed.

I had spent all my life around the club, so to be free to be there now was better for me that any medication. My doctors certainly encouraged this. For the club to allow me into the inner sanctum was a testimony to how remarkably inclusive sport can be. The kindness confirmed the love I feel for the club. I was so grateful for being embraced in such a time.

The clear positive for me of the breakdown was the fact that I was not working. This meant for the first time I could go about my daily life without worrying about my IA issues. I could wake up every day and not have the normal fear I would about soiling and incontinence. I could go to the toilet when I needed. For the first time in my life I had the sense of what living a normal life could be. By going to North at set times I could plan my toilet issues, which was liberating and confidence building.

After a while of this unusual therapy I was able to undertake part time work with the ANZ bank but only a few weeks into the time I was overwhelmed to receive an offer for my fantasy job. I had coped OK with the workload at the bank and was pleased with my progress. After only three weeks in the new job I went down to North to catch up with Jude and while I was there, the football manager who I had known for years inquired about my health. He had heard from my dad that I had resumed part-time work and he had spoken to Jude who confirmed I was doing well. I told him that I was feeling so much better and enjoying doing the casual work. He then asked me to join him in his office where he advised me that with the recent changes in the coaching and football departments, the new coach, Dean Laidley, wanted the club to appoint a part-time Facility Manager. That person would liaise with the coaches for all training sessions regarding training equipment etc., as well as coordinate the players match day uniforms and provide other administrative duties allocated.

He then dropped the bombshell. He said that his executive believed I would be the perfect candidate. He suggested my history with the club as a volunteer staff member (Reserve Grade Team Manager 1987-1991), as well as my knowledge of the club culture and the passion that I and my family had for the club made me the perfect candidate.

To say I was gob smacked would be an understatement, as for me this was my absolute dream role. I walked out of his office on a cloud to see Jude. As soon as I saw her, her beaming face told me she was in the know. I went straight to her and we embraced in a tear-filled hug.

Rather than ring mum and dad, I wanted to tell them in person. I knew how much the news would mean. The news of my part-time job stunned and delighted them. I also shared the news with Dr. Dammery and Dr. Hocking and they were pleased for my chances of recovery in this new environment. My only regret was that my grandpa Tom wasn't around to see this happening. He would have loved me working at North.

All the staff, players and coaches at North were extremely positive about my appointment which gave me a much-needed boost in confidence. I also felt safe because I lived so close. I couldn't have had a better working situation, as I wasn't chained to a desk and I felt I could control my working environment. I also had Jude there for the training sessions and she was keeping an eye on me, which was very reassuring.

I had a period where it was a battle for me but thankfully my doctors and family got me through without it affecting my job. I was still in vulnerable mental health, but I adopted the same strategy I had with my IA and followed the football adage and just took things 'one day at a time'.

By the end of the season, the football manager asked if I would like to take on the job on a full-time basis. The club was pleased with my performance and they could foresee an expansion of my role. I was delighted with the offer, immediately accepting but privately holding concerns about my capacity. I had two weeks' holiday leave due, so that enabled me to talk it over with my doctors and they supported my decision to accept the full-time role. Although it was now to become a full-time commitment, the truth be known was that I didn't think of it as a job, as North was my passion, it was a working hobby for me, and the saviour of my sanity.

I subsequently resumed as a full-time employee as of the start of November 2003. It was three months' shy of two years since I had left my job in the bank as a totally broken man. I was fortunate to have my own office which allowed me total independence and I could manage my IA in this best of working environments. I had immediate access to a toilet which enabled me to keep going back and forth without being noticed. This made life so much easier for me mentally, because if my secret had been revealed in the 'boys club' football culture I am sure I would not have survived.

By early 2004, feeling entrenched in the culture of the club, I was asked to be a part of a working committee for a big function that the club had planned for March 2005. It was to be a celebration of the NMFC history and the intention was to invite every living player who had played a senior game, as well as a family representative of any deceased players. Given my passion for the club and the club's history, I was honored to be part of the committee.

The function was subsequently called The North Story and was to become one of the major events of the club's history. I embraced the role and it became an enormous part of my life over the ensuing 15 months. It became an obsession for me as I was determined to find as many past player and family members as possible.

Leading up to my 40th birthday party in May 2004 I visited a past North player at his business office. I caught the elevator up to Arnold's office and after the meeting took the elevator to the ground floor. I turned left to walk out of the building and instead of walking through the glass sliding door, I walked straight into a massive pane of glass. Fortunately, I had bounced out of the elevator and this assisted me greatly as my knees and forehead must have made the preliminary impact. This resulted in me lurching forward thereby avoiding a massive sheet and shards of glass coming down on me. I could hear some women screaming as I fell to my knees about six feet from the building. As people ran to my assistance the realization of my condition hit me. There was blood everywhere and I was bleeding profusely from both of my legs and my forehead.

After a short time I had composed myself and we had stemmed the bleeding. I was fortunate that there weren't any deep cuts which required stitching. I was particularly sore on both my knees and there were glass fragments sticking out of my skin which I knew would require medical attention.

When I got back to the club, everyone had heard about my adventure and wanted to see how I looked. Typical of a footy club environment everyone thought it was hilarious. The next few days were a bit of a blur as I had to get everything organized for the party plus contend with the after effects of my misadventure.

In March 2005, I was incredibly fortunate to attend what was one of the highlights of my life when just over 3,500 fellow North

Melbourne people arrived at The North Story function at Melbourne's Exhibition Building. For me it was culmination of a year's effort to locate as many living past players and relatives of deceased past players. I am proud to say that of the 912 players (living and deceased) who were eligible I helped locate approximately 80% of living players and 50% of relatives of deceased players.

The absolute highlight and one that will stay for me forever was the hour before the function officially began. It was arranged for every past player who attended the function to be able to gather in a separate area on the 1st floor of the Exhibition Building. For me, as someone who has loved the club with such a passion all my life to see all my past heroes and players together was a dream come true. It was so great to be there with my dad who had been made a NMFC Life Member in 1990. Seeing so many past players greet dad so warmly and enthusiastically just added to what was already a magical experience.

A few months later in July, unfortunately I had a relapse with my mental health. I had started to feel vulnerable once again after the letdown of The North Story function and I tried to hang in here. But it all became too much for me again and I had another breakdown resulting in me having to take three weeks' sick leave. The club was fantastic as they were fully aware of my mental health issues, so I didn't feel the vulnerability I did when at the bank regarding job security.

The one thing that I know for certain and need people to understand is that when dealing with depression you become very selfish. It is such a personal illness that it's hard to deal with your own thoughts and demons. Accommodating anyone else's problems or issues becomes impossible. I needed people to understand and be there for me but when the roles were reversed, I found I could offer nothing. I know I frustrated and disappointed many family and friends with this attitude and I would love to be able to apologize to all of them.

The one thing that I did feel some attachment to, as silly as it sounds, was my bed. Many times, when I could not face the world I would lay in bed, away from what frightened me.

By October 2007, due to my ongoing mucous leakage issues I made an appointment to see Prof Polglase to see if he would perform some surgical intervention. The leakage was as bad now as I had ever experienced and was making life exceedingly difficult. He was more than happy for me to have the same surgery as last time in the hope it would be of benefit to me, but with the proviso once again that there were no guarantees.

Unfortunately, I had to stay in Hospital for three days after the surgery as this time he had to cut and trim a lot more mucosa from my rectal wall which resulted in a lot more pain and bleeding. The recovery took a lot longer at home as well, and I required one-month sick leave from work. As always, the club was 100% supportive.

In November 2008, I had an appointment to see Dr. Dammery (pictured), and he advised me that he would be retiring within a month. I can't describe the feeling that went through my mind and body. I was in total shock and couldn't believe what I was hearing. I had imagined that he would always be a part of my life.

I made sure I saw him one last time before he retired and as I sat in his waiting room, I reflected on the impact he had made on my life. I had had a minimum of 15 appointments each year with him for all my adult life. His influence and importance was immeasurable. When we met for the last time it was an incredibly emotional time for both of us. This man hadn't been just my Doctor, he was my third parent; he was my confidante; my psychiatrist; my marriage counsellor; my protector; my lifeline; and most of all he was my friend.

When the appointment was over, I stood up to shake his hand for the last time. He gently assured me *'a shake won't do it'* and grabbed me in a huge hug. His farewell, so permeated by his warmth and generosity, will stay with me as long as I live.

Sadly, he would not be there for the next twist in my awkward life.

Chapter 12 - The Biggest Rupture

After Dr. Dammery retired, I had to make the decision on who would be my new GP and because of my relationship with Dr. Con Mitropoulos at North Melbourne Football Club where he was the Club Doctor, this was an easy decision.

By early May 2009 however I was losing my capacity to meet my work obligations again. I had been under immense pressure and I had foolishly taken on more roles and responsibiblities and was now also working on match days. This meant I was working at least one day on a weekend, and when we were playing interstate, it meant I was working 7 days in a week.

I had a couple of distressing bowel experiences while I was interstate over the years and I only skated through thanks to Dr. Con. The pressure I was under when interstate was immense as the environment was out of my control and my bowel was much more dangerous in new settings. I also was required to undertake the heavy physical work requirements of loading and unloading the club's match day and training equipment. My back was becoming a further cause of frustration and I was knocking on the physiotherapists door every week for help.

There is no doubt that my back issues could also be traced to my Anorectal Malformation, as is evidenced by my medical records relating to issues with my coccyx and vertebrae at birth.

After extensive discussions at the club it was agreed that I should have a temporary desk job on a part-time basis: back to working three days per week. I was again able to have my own office which assisted my IA concerns. I was so grateful that the club still wanted me to be employed in some capacity.

I changed to my part-time role on 18th May 2009 and even though I was still dealing with my mental health issues, I felt so much more comfortable and most importantly, safer. As the club was in the process of building a brand new multi million dollar facility, I was dealing with the Project Manager closely in my role as Facility Manager.

I agreed to resume my full time role in November 2009 and I got through the next few months. But in mid-April 2010 I faced the next catastrophe emerging from what would seem a minor incident to others. With 30 minutes to game time I realised I had packed the wrong coloured shorts for the teams uniform. In the highly professional environment of AFL football this would have meant both a fine and some ridicule for the club and certainly for me.

The next fifteen minutes were the most panicked of my life, as I had to rush back to North Melbourne to grab the correct shorts. I had one of the other staff members, Mick come with me and he settled me somewhat. Thanks to his calming voice and support we were able to collect the shorts and return to the arena a mere five minutes before the team were due to run on to the ground. I did not get to see this because I had collapsed onto the concrete, passing out for some minutes.

Dr. Con heard I had collapsed, and found me looking shockingly pale. He helped me to my feet and walked me into the rooms. Thankfully the players weren't there as I was feeling totally humiliated. The coach, Brad Scott came up to me and assured me that it would not be an issue. I will forever be thankful for his supportive words at that time, but I couldn't shake the feeling of absolute panic and anxiety.

Later Dr. Con explained that I had suffered a severe panic attack which had caused my fall. The following morning after fitful sleep I woke feeling incredibly anxious and depressed. By the middle of the day it had all became too much for me and in an act of complete self hatred I grabbed a knife and started to cut myself. I made two cuts approximately 50mm long at the base of my left thumb and deep enough until I made sure I felt pain and there was plenty of blood. I was replacing mental pain with physical pain. I was punishing myself for my failure. Next morning I avoided the staff because I was so embarrassed about what had occured. My cuts were on full show and, I realise now that, sub conciously I was sending out a cry for help. Sadly no one could see the affect it was having on my mind, just as no one could see my IA scars.

In the afternoon my manager came down to my office and chatted about the shorts debacle. He was understanding and acknowledged that they had not anticipated how much the facility component of my job would be so demanding. We agreed that the juggle of responsibilities was partly to blame for my oversight.

He then looked at my hand, and asked what happened. I realised I was caught out and after he had checked whether I had made an appointment with my psychiatrist, his next comment chilled me to the bone. " I need to know you are not wacko!" he challenged. In my fragile state and through a veil of fear, I knew my days at the club were numbered from that moment.

The next day, Dr. Con was at the club and I showed him my cuts. He was greatly concerned and we spoke briefly about why I had self harmed. He counselled me regarding the 'wacko' comment and was clearly distressed with the implications. When I saw Dr. Hocking several days later he also became agitated in a way I had not seen before over the comment.

Back at work of course I felt like a complete failure again. This time it was different. There were no excuses, I was responsible for what had happened even though the issue had been forgotten at work. I also became obsessed with the recurring thought that everyone must have believed I was wacko.

I had survived working at North for nine years because of my ability to control my environment. Now with a new building and further adjustments to my job because of my mental condition I felt vulnerable again. My new desk job was in an open plan office environment and I knew I would be under notice at all times.

It bought back all my old insecurities regarding my IA and my secret being exposed, as I would be sitting close to people once again. I had lost the security of the sense of safety I had for so many years working in an office alone, so the anxiety of having an accident or smelling came flooding back.

In the first week in this new setting I found my anxiety levels rising as each day went by. It reminded me of the analogy Dr. Dammery used when he first diagnosed me with depression. When the water of anxiety overflows the glass, there is no stopping it. I was feeling the glass filling as each hour went by that week and I had seemingly no control. On Friday 7th May 2010 at 11.00am, my glass overflowed.

This would be my last day working at my beloved North Melbourne. I was sitting at my desk and I felt a wave of emotion go through my body and I bolted to the toilet. Once there, the tears were uncontrollable, and I knew my time was over; I couldn't keep going. I gradually composed myself and then walked downstairs as I knew Dr. Con was there. I motioned to him to come over to me and he immediately understood. Quietly, and I know sadly, he went upstairs and reported that he was sending me home.

I left the Club and spent the next few days consulting with Dr. Con, Dr. Hocking and mum and dad. Despite the distress, we all knew this period of my life, so full with the camaraderie and tension of world class sport was now closed to me. The following Monday I rang my great friend Jennie at the club and told her that I would not be returning. She was disappointed for me, but she had seen firsthand my struggles at times over the last nine years and had been incredibly supportive to me. She encouraged me to put my health first.

Once again Dr. Hocking advised me that from a medical perspective, I was no longer in a fit state to work in any capacity. In a call to Dr. Con he confirmed Dr. Hocking's recommendation.

He also agreed that he would meet my manager and instruct him that I would resign due to my health concerns. It was over. I had lost my dream job at North. I was in no fit state to be working. I had absolutely no idea what was going to happen next. A copy of the email that my Manager sent to all the staff at North is my strongest memory as I left my second home.

"We would just like to let everyone know that as of today Greg Ryan has officially handed in his resignation citing personal health reasons as the catalyst of this decision.

I am sure we would all like to offer Greg the best of luck in his pursuit of good health which I am sure will eventuate after a good recuperative period. Greg has made a significant contribution to the club over a number of years in his many roles including, managing our Property processes, looking after our Player Appearances and his fantastic work in Managing a dilapidated facility at Arden Street, confronting all types of hurdles including fire and rain damage, then being the conduit for the Football Dept. as the new facility was being built and initially managed.

Greg has asked me to pass on his best wishes to James, Euge and Brad in their Leadership Roles of North Melbourne whilst also acknowledging the fantastic support and friendship that he has received from his work colleagues over the journey here at North.

Feel free to text Greg in the short term and after a few weeks give him a bell to offer your support and well wishes. He will continue to support the Mighty Roos in his usual passionate manner and as time goes on we will see him at the various North Melbourne games.

Good Luck mate we will miss you".

Chapter 13 - Staring into the Abyss

It took me a few weeks to comprehend my new reality. I had a flurry of appointments with my Doctors and after consultations it was agreed that due to my ongoing physical and mental health issues and my disrupted work history that I should formally apply the for the Government Disability Support Pension (DSP).

Like most people with mental health problems the last thing I was thinking about was my medium or long-term future. I knew I had three months of income due to my long service and annual leave entitlements, but my sole focus was trying to get through each day. I was advised that when applying for the DSP I was required to make an appointment with the nearest Centrelink office and that was quickly scheduled for two days later.

I was anxious about the appointment, mainly because I was unaware of the process involved. I knew I had my doctor's confidence that I had a strong case and given my distraught state of health I believed that it would be simple. Standing in the queue I was hit with the brutal reality of where my life had come. The Centrelink officer was pleasant as I gave my personal details but became a lot more serious as we discussed my claim. My anxiety levels shot through the roof and my legs began to shake uncontrollably. He advised me that I would be required to attend a compulsory appointment with a Job Capacity Assessor for an independent assessment.

As I write this now it seems I should have been prepared but it seemed to me at the time that I was under investigation for the crime of having my world crash. Several days later, and after another consultation with my long-suffering doctors, I had my appointment with the independent assessor. My assessor was a young woman with no medical qualifications. Again, describing and detailing my bowel condition and the associated issues was incredibly confronting and upsetting for me. I also had to revisit all my mental health issues and the effect they had on my daily life.

To expose myself in such a way to a total stranger was excruciating. I had protected my secret with such discipline all my life. To be questioned so intensely was extremely difficult for me, as I felt under attack. I was being forced to justify why I had 'survived' working as long as I had and why I wasn't able to work now. Perhaps it was a valid question for an outsider, but I felt my medical record might have indicated some powerful reasons why my nervous breakdown was always inevitable.

I was incredibly naïve to believe that my completed application detailing my conditions along with Dr. Hocking's report would be sufficient. It now shows how mentally fragile I was, because if I was more stable, I would have been readier for the interview and the result.

At an appointment with Dr. Hocking three weeks later he advised me that he had received notification from Centrelink that my claim for the DSP had been rejected. He handed me the document which he had received. It was devastating to me. I sincerely hope there are not too many other distressed people receiving such a report.

Rejection of your claim for Disability Support Pension

- To be eligible to receive the Disability Support Pension, you must be unable to work 15 or more hours a week for at least the next 2 years. A decision has been made that you are not eligible for Disability Support Pension because you are able to work 15 or more hours a week within the next 2 years.

- In making this decision we took into account your skills, qualifications, work history and the medical evidence you and your doctor gave us.

- You may, however, be eligible to receive other payments and services from Centrelink, for example, Newstart Allowance or a Low-Income Health Care Card. Please call us on the number shown on this letter so we can discuss any other options that may be available to you.
- This decision has been made under social security law.

Assessment Summary

- **The Conditions which are fully diagnosed, treated and stabilized are:**
  Depression and Anxiety; Rectal condition

- **Client Presentation:**
  The client attended interview alone and was punctual. The client wore clean attire and communicated clearly throughout the interview, indicating good insight into the impact of symptoms on their functioning. The client appeared to be significantly shaking during the entire assessment; he was unable to hold his hands and was physically shaking for the entire assessment. The client appeared extremely nervous and agitated however was polite and friendly. The client cooperated throughout the interview and agreed to participate in the interview voluntarily.

- **Social:**
  The client is a 46-year-old man who currently resides alone in his grandmother's home (the client's grandmother is now in a nursing home). The client reported that their current accommodation is stable and that there are no financial concerns as he received a payout from work that can sustain him. The client has contact with family members and friends. The client also reported that they have a current driver's license and a car, and is able to competently use public transport. The client does not substance abuse issues, and does not have any legal issues.

- *Assessor Recommendations:*

  Based on the information contained within this report the assessor recommends that the following occur:
  It is likely that the client will be successful in obtaining and maintaining employment within the next two years. It is the recommendation of the assessor that the client have a work capacity of 0-7 hours until 08/10/2010 to allow the client to care for their health to avoid further symptoms arising. After this time, a baseline work capacity of 15-22 hours would be suitable for this client to allow the client to care for their health to ensure no further deterioration.

As the client was observed as being agitated and anxious during the assessment, it is recommended that the client view the report with a qualified professional e.g. Psychologist or Psychiatrist who can understand the meaning of the information in the report and to avoid misinterpretation or personalization of material recorded.

Dr. Hocking told me he was incredulous after he read the full report from the Job Capacity Assessor. His anger on my behalf was an emotion I had not witnessed from him previously. For me, this rejection was just another blow to my already mental fragility.

I was thankful however that the assessor recognized my vulnerability and had the correspondence sent directly to Dr.

Hocking. It was hard enough dealing with the rejection in my safest place and I don't want to contemplate how I would have handled it if I had opened the letter when alone.

Dr. Hocking then advised me that he was very strong in the opinion that the denial of my DSP application was outrageous and that we must appeal the decision. He mentioned that he hadn't had any previous patient's application for the DSP denied. He added that he felt my case was a lot more severe than many of his other patients who had applied successfully.

My first instinct was that it was all going to be too hard and I doubted if I had the physical and mental capacity to go through the process again. But as Dr. Hocking was so adamant, I agreed that I would investigate the process to appeal the decision.

I left his rooms and immediately rang mum and dad and told them of the disappointing news. Once I told them of Dr. Hocking's reaction they were glad we were going to appeal the decision.

My next call was to Dr. Con's room to ask him to call me when he was free of patients. That call came later that night and he was as shocked as Dr. Hocking had been. He was fully supportive of the decision to appeal and offered supporting documentation.

Both he and Dr. Hocking were of the belief that for my original application, a report from Dr. Hocking would be sufficient. He also suggested I contact Greg Buck who was a psychologist who had worked at the club and was compassionate and understanding.

I contacted Centrelink to advise them that I was appealing the original decision and they advised that I needed to once again make an appointment and apply in person at the South Melbourne office. Fortunately, a close friend of mine, Les Cameron, who I came to know through our common North Melbourne history offered to join me for that interview.

When I was called, Les came with me and, seeing my discomfort, basically took over. Les told the officer that he was here as my advocate. The officer then advised for this to happen I must nominate Les officially as my nominee, which I confirmed, and we filled out the necessary documents.

Les was amazing, firmly demanding to know the appeals process required. It was all a bit of a blur to me and even though Les was there, I was very shaky and anxious. The officer advised us that I would no longer be contacted by Centrelink and that any correspondence would go directly to Les. When I look back I realize how each of these steps from authorities serves to belittle you and rock your confidence further. Nevertheless, it was a great relief to me to have someone who would add their voice to mine.

We were given application forms I had to pass on to Dr. Hocking and Dr. Con to complete, and they both agreed that Greg Buck's support would also be crucial. We organized our case as best possible and Les submitted the appeal documents on my behalf. Two months later, after some prompting of Centrelink from Les, I finally received a verdict on my appeal. The original DSP decision was going be reversed and I was now considered eligible.

My first reaction was relief and I thanked the official that rang. He then stated in a most forceful manner that the only reason I was successful in my appeal was due to a phone call he had made to Dr. Hocking that morning. After he had gone through the original decision he was initially of the opinion it was the correct one, predominantly due to relative young age and my work history. But, as he had received such strong medical submissions, he chose to contact Dr. Hocking directly and after a lengthy discussion with Dr. Hocking that morning, he was convinced by Dr. Hocking that I was medically qualified to receive the DSP. Once again, Dr. Hocking had been my savior.

The next day I received the official letter from Centrelink, advising me that I was now eligible for the Disability Support Pension and that my payments would be backdated to the original processed date of my application some 4 months earlier.   Although I was delighted with the financial bonus, for me, there was no amount of compensation could make up for the mental anguish of the last three months and the angst I caused my family, friends and doctors.

So, again I had some certainty in my life. It was bitter sweet. I desperately needed the certainty of the DSP for my future, but I felt a sense of sadness and failure as well. I had spent all my life trying to be normal, but was now officially labelled as disabled.

Strangely, while I knew I was very different from most people, I had never thought of myself as disabled. This was the day the differences finally caught up with me.

I began to learn to live with a stigma that goes along with being viewed as a "welfare case" in this society. Predominately I was guilt ridden because I was not working. I knew there were no discernable signs of illness but suddenly I wore a mental illness tag to accompany my obscure physical shame.

Chapter 14 - The End of Surgery

In June of 2014, I had received a "Bowel Cancer Screening Kit" in the mail. I now know that one is automatically sent to any Australian citizen who turns 50 years of age. When I received the kit however my fears of a colonoscopy and colostomy bags and the physical pain and discomfort I had experienced over my lifetime triggered a panic attack.

I discussed my fears with psychiatrist Dr. Mark Walterfang as I needed to understand why I had such deep fears. He explained that it was perfectly understandable due to my history and that my bowel issues were   core to my anxiety issues. He suggested that I was basically suffering from post-traumatic stress disorder (PTSD). Sadly, these stresses were not going to ease up quickly as the next few months were about to prove.

I was having significant issues again with my soiling and mucous leakage which was leading me back to deep depression. With Dr. Con's support, I began a series of tests and proposals. Eventually this lead back to the need for a colonoscopy. I arranged that Professor Adrian Polglase at the Cabrini Hospital would do the procedure as he had performed three prior surgeries on me. Leading up to the appointment I started to seriously think about discussing with Professor Polglase if there was any value in having further surgery to assist with minimizing the leakage and soiling. As soon as I was called into his office and shook his hand again, it was like I had only seen him yesterday. He was very sympathetic to my current situation and suggested that I had three options. These were stark. I could choose between a colonoscopy test and doing nothing; an advanced surgical procedure called a "Transanal Haemorrhoidal Dearterialisation" (THD)"; or stoma surgery with a permanent colostomy bag attached to my body.

He believed strongly that the colostomy bag was the most beneficial for me and would allow me to have a much greater quality of life. He outlined various cases of patients where it has changed their life for the better going down this track, but for me it was putting up the "white flag" and surrendering to my condition, so it wasn't an option for me while I still had an option.

As I had agreed to have the colonoscopy, we agreed that it was a worthwhile for Professor Polglase to perform the THD surgery at the time of undertaking the Colonoscopy. After a preparatory examination, the Professor emphasized that once again that this would be "experimental" surgery procedure due to my IA condition being so rare.

By May I was lying on the operating table getting prepared for theatre and Prof. Polglase advised that he could not find reference to any patient with an Imperforate Anus who had had this surgical procedure performed. He reiterated that this was an "experimental surgery" with no guarantees of success but we both agreed it was a worthwhile exercise. Once again, I was being classified as "rare" by the medical profession. Not quite the comfort you wish as you go under anesthetic.

When I awoke, I was advised that the colonoscopy was all clear with no polyp's present. This was a great relief, but the next 24 hours were horrific. I had an uncontrollable sequence of bowel accidents. Apparently, my body had not reacted well to the surgery and I was in physical and mental trauma. The physical discomfort was horrific and shameful, but the mental impact was worse. All my memories of my childhood when these accidents were a regular occurrence flooded back.

Prof. Polglase arrived at the ward around 4.30pm and I was certainly relieved to see him. He had been told by the Nurses that I had the bowel accidents, but he said he wasn't disappointed to hear that news. He explained that he had found with this surgery the greatest risk was to suffer from severe constipation resulting in bowel impaction. Then the only treatment would have been a rectal enema which to me was a fate worse than death.

The weeks dragged by and there seemed little improvement in my condition and the follow up appointment reinforced this. Professor Polglase confirmed the surgery has been unsuccessful. He once again canvassed the idea of a colostomy bag, but I told him I was not prepared to look at that option at this point. Instead we discussed more surgery. He described "Ligation and excision of mucous from my bowel lining" and I agreed to have this follow up surgery once my body had healed. Ironically, as irrational as this sounds, I realised these manipulations of my body were giving me something to anticipate. The hope that my body would one day improve was a ray of optimism in each of my days of mental distress.

Unfortunately, there were also other issues. My prostate and penile discharge concerns were also back to haunt me and Dr. Con organised an appointment with Urologist Mr. Paul Ruljancich at his rooms in Box Hill. When I walked in to Mr. Ruljancich's room the first thing he said to me was "well you are an interesting and complex case", to which I replied, "well you're not the first person who has said that to me". I asked if he had ever had an Imperforate Anus patient before and he said that he hadn't. I had taken my surgery notes from the Royal Children's Hospital to give the Doctor an idea of the "mechanics" of my Anus and Genitals.

Dr. Ruljancich examined my stomach and genitals. This surprised me as I was expecting the usual prostate examination. Instead he checked my scars and advised that he wished to perform two separate examinations under sedation in hospital. The first was what is called a "Flexible Cystoscopy" which involves a "telescope" be inserted into the eye of the penis which travels through to my bladder and urethra for a thorough internal examination. Of course, the thought of this was highly disturbing especially with impending surgery with Prof. Polglase already scheduled. There was to be only 8 days between the two hospital stays.

I was eventually admitted to Epworth Eastern Hospital to undergo a Flexible Cystoscopy procedure on my bladder as well as an internal examination of my prostate. I was extremely trepidant as I flashed back to the similar experiences of my childhood, but I was glad that I might have some relief from the chronic discharges that had marred my life.

I managed my way through the procedure with the help of an empathetic anesthetist and the nurses and was discharged the next day. Soon after I was advised by Mr. Ruljancich that both the examination of bladder urethra and prostate came through totally fine. Less comforting was the news that while there was nothing sinister the discharge issue was just something that I would have to live with.

A few days later I admitted myself to hospital again at the Cabrini Hospital for my next scheduled surgery by Prof. Polglase. I realised that this was to be my 16th lifetime surgery. I hoped my body would this time respond successfully.

I walked into the theatre and was welcomed by Prof. Polglase with his warm and reassuring smile and felt totally at ease. After the operation Prof. Polglase came to my bedside and assured me that everything had gone well. Unhappily I was about to experience another harried night.

At around 9.00pm I needed to urinate, so I got out of the bed and put on my pajama pants and walked very slowly and gingerly to the nurses' desk. I asked for directions to the toilet, so another nurse held my arm and guided me to the toilet which was at least 30 metres away. I couldn't believe that the only toilet available was that distant and it seemed to be used by both patients and visitors. My mind immediately went into panic mode again thinking how will I cope if I need to get to this toilet. As I was in a post-operative ward and not a private room due to the Hospital being full, I quickly felt demoralized both physically and mentally.

I was just too shattered inside and felt totally defeated. I needed a distraction, so I got on my iPad and put a post on my personal Facebook page.

"Well, surgery has happened, and Prof was happy with how it went, so we will just wait and see now. No pics tonight, as I look a bit worse for wear. Not sure how the night ahead will be considering the Hospital is chockers and I'm in a post op ward of nine patients. Thanks for the support you have all given me, it truly does make a difference. I'm a very lucky man to have friends like you all".

The replies I got were so wonderful and made me feel very special and loved. This was just what I needed as I could feel myself getting more anxious and depressed as the night wore on. In the middle of the night I had awakened to a sharp pain on the back of my left hand. It took me a moment to realize that I had somehow ripped the "stent/needle" which was still there from the surgery and blood was spurting everywhere straight from the vein. I grabbed the remote and buzzed for the nurse, who arrived within ten seconds and by that stage I had my hand and the sheets covered in blood. She removed the needle and placed gauze on my hand.

Blood was soaking my bedsheets when Prof. Polglase arrived to see me just after 7.30am amongst the chaos. We had a quick discussion about the procedures he had followed and agreed to an appointment one month later.

I had been reasonably comfortable for most of that month but on the eve of meeting with the Professor I had a huge discharge of blood with my faeces and mucous. I had been able to record photos for Professor Polglase and he was shocked at what he was looking at. He was concerned at the amount of blood evident. He explained that he was disappointed for me that it appeared the surgery had not yielded any improvement.

It is a confronting moment when a very experienced and respected colorectal surgeon says to you that we have tried the only two surgical options available and they haven't been successful. I respected his honesty but it still hit me very hard when he explained that when patients come and see him he basically can give them an answer to their problems. But as his only IA patient he had no solutions. Once again, it reinforced that an IA patient is never fixed!

I thanked him for everything he had tried to do for me and as I walked back to my car I felt totally exhausted mentally. I had put myself through so much over the last six months in the vanquished hope that I may be able to improve my quality of life. Now I knew for certain that these physical burdens were not going away. I had to find a way to use the good experiences and cope psychologically.

By March of 2016 my emotional life had indeed improved thanks to the IA group support. Dr Con alerted me to the work of Colorectal Surgeon called Ms. Adele Burgess. She had been performing a surgical procedure she specialised in called "Sacral Nerve Stimulation", which was targeted at people with my symptoms. Although after my two surgeries the previous year I had sworn not to have voluntary surgery again I felt a duty to learn as much as I could about this for everyone's sake.

Before advancing this, I had the delightful experience of meeting with my former RCH Pediatric Surgeon, Mr. Justin Kelly (pictured) It had been 32 years since the last time I saw him as patient. I spent 90 minutes with him along with a current Paediatric Surgeon at RCH, Dr. Sebastian King. One of the interesting things that emerged from our discussion was agreement from Mr. Kelly and  Sebastian with my proposition that there was a crucial need for a much better medical transition from paediatric care to adult care. I reminded them that my family was left to fend for ourselves after I left RCH care.

Sebastian used the great metaphor that "Adult Colorectal Surgeons deconstruct; Paediatric Colorectal Surgeons reconstruct". This was a perfect description as IA patients are caught in the middle needing "maintenance" and continued psychological care from an adult perspective. It was encouraging to hear Sebastian acknowledge that the paediatricians now recognise the need to address the children's emotional health as well as their physical comfort.

The most transfixing part of the meeting for me was when Mr. Kelly admitted that rather than telling my parents I was "fixed" he and the other doctors should have told my parents that I was as "fixed as I could be". This subtle word difference would have given us all so much better understanding.

We had all felt that our efforts were inadequate and consequently suffered dreadful emotional torment that could have been avoided. I shudder when I think how much my parents must have borne trying to help me be normal when that was never possible. Mr. Kelly also advised me that my diagnosis as having *"Anal/Rectal Agenesis without Fistula"* was an incredibly rare form of IA.

Mr. Kelly also linked my genital and urological issues when I mentioned that I had no children. Mr. Kelly was not surprised considering my history. He also advised that the urological issues were not really addressed when I was young as focus was on bowel function. This was something that had crossed my mind when my wife and I were trying to start a family but I was so poorly informed I failed to confront the issue effectively.

Our reunion was significant and transforming for all of us I believe. Dr Kelly was pleased to hear of my passion to assist families and the medical fraternity, by sharing my life experiences and advocating for creative change. I realised how much we had all learnt and somehow my struggle seemed more meaningful as a result.

On the 22nd April, I had my appointment with colorectal surgeon Ms. Adele Burgess and I felt very comfortable with her immediately, which was so important for me. We discussed my medical history and my current bowel management regimes. She reviewed the referral letter from Dr. Con, and the recent surgical reports from Prof. Polglase and asked if I had considered a colostomy bag. It now seemed the inevitable question. I assured her this was a long way down my priority list and I am sure she understood. She then described the SNS procedure and its potential benefits.

We agreed that the chances of me being a candidate given my lack of muscle control were slim. Nevertheless, I decided that I was willing to undertake the relevant tests under general anesthetic. I was under no illusions that I would be suitable, but for me it was another opportunity for another colorectal surgeon to examine me and give her opinion of my IA issues. There was the bonus of having tests done that I had not had as an adult.

Ms. Burgess could do the tests within four days, so very suddenly I was in the waiting room of the Warringah Private hospital awaiting more tests. It certainly had become a familiar way to spend my life. My parents were skeptical and concerned about another series of surgical tests and mum was still trying to talk me out of it when we were driving to the hospital. I knew I needed to try all I could to improve the quality of my life. I knew I was substituting these medical procedures for the sense of deep seeded worthlessness I felt. I was trying like crazy to justify my existence. After I awoke from the testing Ms. Burgess explained that not having a functioning internal or external sphincter meant I didn't have the necessary muscle control for the SNS procedure.

I had a follow up appointment with Ms. Burgess 2 weeks later and found that the four separate tests she had done gave me an opportunity to delve deeper into my situation. She advised that the test results indicated the only surgical option I had left would be to have a colostomy bag fitted. She also advised that I also would need to have my rectum totally removed and my anal opening closed.

Due to my unique anatomy, Ms. Burgess explained that without this closure (stitching up my anus) I would still have mucous leakage. I left the appointment feeling grateful that Ms. Burgess was so honest and open with me. I also felt a sense of sadness as all my options were now exhausted.

Over the ensuing days I became more depressed, anxious and vulnerable. I hardly left the house simply needing to stay in my safe zone. My next appointment with my psychiatrist cleared the fog. He explained the failed tests had radically diminished the final rays of hope that I had been clasping. By being told that my only real option now was the permanent colostomy bag and having my rectum removed, all my optimism and hope had gone. He reminded me that in effect nothing had really changed over all those years. I had survived this far and I would continue to survive.

I had given physical change my best shot over the previous twelve months through the repeated surgical interventions. Hope was gone from a medical perspective but what was about to occur next in my life was something no surgical intervention could have ever offered me.

Chapter 15 - Victim No More

The 6th July 2016 was just an ordinary Wednesday, but for me it was momentous. I had lived for 19,052 days and for all that time my secret was confined to my family members and my doctors. But that had now changed. Over the previous two years I had started to talk openly with other IA adults online, but I was still very guarded. Due to my impending trip to attend the Conference in Orlando USA, the day of my secret's release had arrived. I had an obligation to go public and I was finally ready to face my secret. So, with much trepidation, I posted my revelations on my personal Facebook Page for every one of my almost 200 friends to view. There was no turning back.

"As you all know I've had medical issues all of my life, but only over the last couple of years I've started to open up bit by bit. But now is the time where I stop hiding behind my secret and share it with everyone, not just very few select people who I have entrusted. The medical condition is known as an Anorectal Malformation (ARM), it's most commonly known as Imperforate Anus (IA).

In simple terms, I was born without any anal opening and had to have many surgeries to correct the issue. This Sunday, 10th July, I leave to go on a trip to the USA where I will be attending a conference in Orlando, Florida held by a wonderful USA based support organisation called the Pull Thru Network. This is a truly

*incredible personal opportunity for me to meet other IA adults
but also to be able to share my experiences with parents of IA
kids who have their lives ahead of them and to raise awareness
and understanding of IA.*

*For me to be the advocate I want to be for the IA community it
is only fair that I publicly put myself out there and not hide in
shame and embarrassment as I always done until the last
couple of years. Wish me luck."*

Greg

I had joined the PTN Support Group website earlier in 2015 after
reading a post on a Facebook IA Group page about the conference
and I immediately felt drawn to it. I investigated further and
subsequently paid a modest   fee to join the PTN group and to be
eligible to attend the Conference.   The USA based **Pull Thru
Network** is dedicated to supporting people born with an Anorectal
Malformation   (ARM),   which   covers   Imperforate   Anus,
Hirschsprung's Disease & Cloaca (females only) and their families.

I discussed the prospect of attending with my colorectal surgeon
(Prof. Adrian Polglase), my GP (Dr. Con Mitropoulos) and my
psychiatrist (Assoc. Prof Mark Walterfang). All were very strongly
of the view that it would be a wonderful opportunity. I booked in
early February having to wait five months but most importantly
having something significant to anticipate. That was so important

as I had had to deal with some very low times over the previous few months and the trip horizon helped me mentally.

So, on the 10th of July I boarded the Qantas flight for an adventure that would again change my life. My primary concern was that I have no bowel accidents while on the plane. I had taken all necessary precautions and had supplies if something occurred. I had planned to arrive early so I could give myself a few days to get over the flight and adjust to a new time zone.

I spent all the Monday in bed suffering from severe jet lag and a strange nervousness. Fortunately, I knew one of the organizers, Executive Director Lori Parker, was already there. I messaged her about 6.00pm that evening and was invited to dinner with her daughter Kaydee and two of the other organizers, Tricia and Tenley. They were incredibly embracing of me and thankful that I had travelled so far to be a part of the conference. By Wednesday I felt the warm friendship and had adapted to the local time zone and felt so excited about the pending arrivals.

This was going to be the biggest of any PTN Conference so far with over 200 people attending, which included kids, teens, adults and PTN parents. As well there were 25 people from the medical fraternity including numerous world-renowned pediatric surgeons who specialize in the ARM field.

I was excited for an extra reason, as I was going to meet face to face with special friends, I had met through the Facebook IA Community. This included Chelsea, who is a PTN adult, aged 30 with whom I had become incredibly close over the previous 12-18 months through sharing our stories and supporting each other across the bad days. Chelsea is also an original member of our IA Facebook Adult group as well as being a nurse. Thus, she provides an extra perspective that is so informative and supportive to us all. What she has endured all her life and still must manage daily is beyond comprehension to me; she is a loving mum to a 3-year-old daughter, a devoted wife as well as a full-time Nurse. She is a genuine hero and knowing what she endures inspires me to not wallow in my own misery.

The other people I was looking forward to meeting were families of two other PTN boys from Alabama and New Jersey with whom I had established a great rapport over the previous twelve months. My chatting to them online had had a positive impact on them and their children I had been told. Apparently, my adult perspective gave them new insights into the boys' experiences. The family from Alabama included Christie and her 12-year-old son Gavin. I had first communicated with Christie after she had posted on the Facebook IA International Support Group page.

The post described how Gavin and his brother were having great trouble interacting which each other. Christie asked if there were any other IA parents with a similar issue. I responded that I would be happy to share my experiences of living with my brother when we were young. That link led me to meet a second family, Michelle & Dave and their 9-year-old son Aiden. They believed that through my insights through Facebook they had gained a greater and more empathetic understanding of Aiden's life.

We all met for breakfast and I felt this incredible sense of belonging build as each minute of our time together sped by. I spent most of Wednesday with them and it was a really special day for me. Later that same day I was told that I had made an unusual impact. I had been introduced to a couple and their 19-year-old daughter who lived with the IA disability early in the afternoon and was advised only a half hour later that the daughter had been inspired by me. Delving further I found she had reported "that Australian guy is so old and he has survived, that gives me such great hope." Well to say I was speechless was an understatement. I'm glad to have helped the young woman but I wasn't too happy to be called an old man I must admit! I posted the comment on Facebook and it caused a lot of laughter amongst my friends.

The Thursday morning started off wonderfully as I met Chelsea for the first time in person. It was such a special moment as we hugged: we had been through so much together over the last twelve months, albeit online. We had a photo taken and it's become one of my favourites because I am sitting and smiling next to a very special friend with whom I have developed a bond. By the end of the conference, Chelsea was telling everyone that she was my little sister. That is exactly how I now view her.

The introduction session for the conference was almost a blur as I was approached by many people seeming to want my attention.

Firstly, I was greeted by Dr. Jeffrey Avansino (Associate Professor of Surgery at University of Washington and an attending Pediatric Surgeon at Seattle Children's Hospital) who had a special interest in Anorectal Malformations. Soon we were joined by Dr. Aaron Garrison, Pediatric Surgeon at Akron Children's Hospital who specializes in colorectal procedures. Both had read my introduction message in the conference handbook and were interested in my story. After the session, I was approached by Dr. Payan Saadai (Assistant Professor of Surgery – UC Davis Medical Centre/Shriners Hospital for Children, Sacramento). I was over the moon by this stage with the interest I had received from the doctors, and it was only the first morning!

I spent time strolling around and chatting to people comfortably. This was a great start for me as I'm normally very socially awkward with complete strangers. For some reason in this highly energetic environment I just felt totally at ease. I was meeting Facebook friends and attending sessions with long titles like: **Navigating the Psychosocial Impact of the Medically Complex Child.** These were of great interest to me but alienated many of us because we were hearing generalizations rather than attending to the burden of constant fear of accidents felt by sufferers.

Sadly, at a more intimate session late on the first day which was for PTN Adults only, the discussion moved to the daily bowel management each person experiences and the topic quickly focused on enemas/flushes. As the subject is incredibly confronting and upsetting to me I just shut down and started to get very anxious and my leg started to shake uncontrollably as it does when I'm in a panic attack stage. I excused myself and left the assembly. The topic of enemas/bowel washouts is an enormous trigger point for many of us and a definite PTSD type situation we have from our childhood.

After the session, I went back to my room because I was rattled so much and needed to clear my head, but by the time I went to dinner I was feeling better. I stayed at dinner until 8pm but them went back to my room, as it was a pretty full on day. I got a message from Chelsea around 9pm asking me how I was, as she could tell the adult session rocked me a bit.

I woke up on the Friday morning feeling very refreshed and my head was clear and headed to breakfast. I took my two binders which had my surgical notes in just in case I ran into Dr. Avansino and Dr. Garrison. Strangely despite my distress the previous night as I walked into the dining room, I was overcome with a real sense of belonging. For the first time in my life I walked into a room and felt like an equal and not a lesser person due to my IA. It was a very empowering feeling and I felt rejuvenated.

Just as I had finished my breakfast, Dr. Garrison approached me to say hello. I reported that I had my surgery notes with me and he immediately invited me to join him and some other doctors at their table. Dr. Garrison introduced me to one of his colleagues, Dr. Belinda Dickie who was the Pediatric Surgeon at the Colorectal Centre of Boston Children's Hospital. When they both had read my surgery notes they both commented on how incredibly detailed they were. I could tell how pleased they were to read them, which gave me an equal pleasure. They discussed some medical terms and I asked Dr. Dickie how different the surgeries are done nowadays compared to mine. She was extremely knowledgeable and explained to me that when I had my pull through surgery, Mr. Nate Myers and Mr. Douglas Stephens did it side to side (horizontally) across my anal area, (which was to be known as the "Stephens procedure" amongst the medical fraternity). Dr. Dickie then explained to me in detail the standard surgical procedure used now which differs from the "Stephens procedure" and was pioneered by Dr. Alberto Pena in the 1980's and is called a "Posterior Sagittal Anorectoplasty" (PSARP).

As I reflected, once our meeting was over, the conference had only been going 24 hours and I was absolutely in no doubt it was going to be life changing for me. I had met friends, fellow sufferers and the medicos that serviced them and I felt that I was an insider in my world rather than an outsider. I had set as my main aim to meet Dr. Marc Levitt, who is recognized universally as one of the most pre-eminent pediatric surgeons relating to ARM. He is currently the Surgical Director at the Centre of Colorectal and Pelvic Reconstruction at Nationwide Children's Hospital in Columbus Ohio.

I had sent Dr. Levitt an email 12 months earlier, after reading that he had been a colleague of one of my Pediatric doctors at the Royal Children's Hospital, Mr. Justin Kelly when Mr. Kelly was a resident at a USA Hospital. I thought he may find my story interesting and he replied he would like to hear more so I emailed him the first three chapters of this manuscript and included all the surgery notes. On the second day of this enchanting conference Dr. Avansino introduced me to Dr. Levitt and to my great delight he had remembered my story and welcomed me warmly. He was keen to hear more and glad that I would be willing to share my story with everyone later at the conference, particularly at the designated session only for PTN Adults and the medical professionals in attendance.

I sat with Chelsea for the next session and I was feeling confident that Dr. Levitt and the others would be interested in my views. The session focused on constipation and I was aware that at some stage that it would become confronting for me once the discussion turned to enemas. The doctors analysed a few different scenarios and described how they addressed the issues of a correct bowel management program for the child. I became more and more anxious as the prevalence of the amount of discussion was focused of the mechanical program. I could absolutely understand from the doctor's perspective that their sole aim was for the child to gain a level of social continence and if that meant an enema regime well so be it. But due to my intense personal experience and trauma of being subjected to a long-term enema regime as a child I felt like I needed to ask a question.

Once the parents had asked their relevant questions, I asked the panel: "Do you as Doctors consider the psychological affects that a continual enema program takes on the child?" I could tell that the question took them all aback somewhat, but I owed it to the kids to ask. They acknowledged that this was a valid issue, but I sensed the doctors didn't want to frighten them due to the topic of psychological health being addressed. I could tell by nods of approval from some parents that it was a real issue. I was glad I asked the question because I realised that this was why I was at the conference. I wanted to raise the mental health issues relating to IA with the medical fraternity and this was my opportunity.

Once the session had finished one of the pediatric surgeons thanked me for being so open and direct on the psychological impacts of enemas. He said it was the first time he had witnessed anyone challenge the conventional wisdom regarding the effects of long-term enemas. Coming from an adult who had lived through the experience he believed this was very powerful data. He was very firm in the belief that the continual rectal enemas would no doubt have a detrimental psychological impact on a child but because of medical politics it was a very difficult issue to address.

I could see both sides, especially knowing the enema program helped to achieve social continence. This lessened the chance of accidents and anxiety which had led to my mental health issues.

I was pleased to hear his perspective as it supported my real-life personal experiences and those of so many other adults. We also discussed going further on the topic by utilizing our IA Adult group, which I have no doubt will reinforce our belief. I suppose I have the view that I don't want any child to go through the pain and suffering of a long-term enema regime that I experienced unless absolutely as a last resort.

We headed off to lunch and although there was a PTN Adult male session on urological concerns scheduled I didn't attend as I was still a bit gun shy from the PTN Adult only session the day before. I had a chat with Chelsea about going to the session and why I was reluctant and that was when the reality hit me: the reason why I was so averse was because there is no doubt I feel lesser of a man due to my genital issues. I just couldn't go to the urological session even though I had so many questions to ask related to that area.

While we were at lunch Chelsea, my other Facebook friend, Alan, and I were chatting about our impending lead roles at the conference that evening. We had all been asked to develop power point presentations and to discuss our personal experiences with all conference attendees.

At the afternoon session for the PTN Adults and medical professionals, I took the lead role as facilitator of the meeting and I was first cab off the rank. As I was about to begin my spiel, Dr. Levitt who was in the audience asked if he could address the attendees before I commenced. To my absolute surprise, Dr. Levitt explained to his fellow medicos how fortunate they all were to have me in attendance. He explained that I was a patient of ARM pioneers in Mr. Stephens and Mr. Kelly who had impacted so greatly on the USA Pediatric Colorectal fraternity when they were visiting "fellows".

He then left me gob smacked when he said, "Greg is a walking museum". I had a tear in my eye to be recognized so generously by Dr. Levitt. I just wish Mr. Stephen, Mr. Kelly and mum and dad had been there as well. I gathered myself and then spoke to the group for ten minutes about my life as an IA Adult, and I really targeted the absolute lack of transition from pediatric to adult care. I emphasised my mental health issues later in life due to the stigma and shame I had felt as I grew. I catalogued the traumatic effects of the enemas, regular hospitalization, bowel accidents, soiling that I faced as a child and addressed my ongoing physical issues. The other IA adults followed with lucid descriptions of their experiences and supported the need for better support regarding transition and mental health.

We also advised the doctors and nurses about our IA Adult Support Group and they were shocked that there was such a resource available to us and, of course, to them. The doctors were very enthusiastic about collaborating with our group going forward and we all became excited about this prospect as we realised our own strength. We anticipated the difference in care responses we might achieve if we systematically shared our life experiences with the medical fraternity. After the formalities doctors were quick to give us their contact details and commit to the IA Adult support group.

I left that session feeling very buoyed and proud that the open dialogue provided by us was about to change lives. Immediately after our overtime session we were hurried to an equivalent session with the teenagers. We walked into the room and apologized to the teens for keeping them waiting. To my surprise there were about 20-25 of them and the boys and girls were sitting on separate sides of the rooms. We introduced ourselves and gave a bit of a biography and confirmed we were there to answer any questions that they may have. I was pleasantly surprised how open they were about discussing issues and it made me so happy to think they had each other. Compared to my isolation at that age this was a wonderful step forward.

We asked for a show of hands of those who had told friends about their condition and we were dazzled that every one of those teenagers raised their hand! We just looked at each other in amazement. I admitted that it had taken me 50 years to have the courage to divulge my condition to anyone and this time they were the ones shocked. I was incredibly happy for them all to realize they weren't alone and didn't have to live with the burden of a secret.

Soon after we joined other delegates in the packed conference room and Chelsea, me and then Alan were introduced for our major presentations. As expected, Chelsea's presentation was brilliant, and I could see how much the audience was responding. I have no doubt she was impacting particularly on the parents of young girls living with cloaca. Considering the kids were in attendance as well, there was little noise as she spoke and used the big screens to show her PowerPoint slides. She got a very warm reception when she completed her presentation.

So, then it was my turn, and even though I was initially anxious when I realized that kids would be in attendance, I was quite relaxed when I stepped up to the lectern. My presentation took a bit longer than I expected. Near the completion of my presentation I read the poem I had written called "*My Secret Life* "and to my incredible surprise, the audience started to clap and then stand. I was very humbled and a bit embarrassed, but I relished and enjoyed the endorsement.

MY SECRET LIFE

I was born with a condition, that no-one could really see
So I kept it as a secret, and hid the real me
To deal with its stigma, or to try and explain
I knew would be too hard, and just cause me more pain

I learnt to live with it, by taking each day by day
Even with the knowledge that it would never go away
I got on with my life, with the hand I got dealt
And adapted and adjusted, not matter how I felt

I'd be lying if I said, it's been an easy ride
But I'm proud to say, I've been able to survive
Then after 50 years, the time came to be
That I unveiled my secret, to those close to me

It was a shock to everyone, as they had no idea at all
But it made me feel proud, as I opened up and stood tall
Then it made me realise, that will all my struggles and fight
I'm proud of what I've achieved living "My Secret Life"

When I sat down, Chelsea advised me that she had videoed some of my speech   and was streaming it live on our Facebook IA Adult group page. Apparently, people from our group were watching my story live across the world. Sitting down in a daze I had an overwhelming feeling of love and acceptance in the room. I gradually transitioned into Alan's speech which was very moving and humorous and also overwhelmingly well received. The parallels of our lives were evident (he is three years older) and I could relate to many things he discussed.

Despite the pleasure and satisfaction from these wonderful moments as we left the conference centre I had barely walked 10 metres when I was bought back to reality with an enormous thud! My body had relaxed and within that ten seconds of leaving that room, I felt the unmistakable feeling of a piece of sneaky stool appear in my rectum. Again, at a peak moment of my life I was reminded of the reality of my condition. It was a special day and one I could not have imagined would ever happen to me. To share such deeply personal experiences in such an open forum with people who understood was so empowering, but I was now paying for it physically. I will not forget Friday 15th July 2016 tinged with the knowledge that no matter how great a day I can be having, I could have to surrender to my IA at any moment.

When I woke early on the Saturday morning and went down for breakfast, I was joined by one of the Doctors and we conversed about the session and how he found it very informative and had appreciated our honesty. As we were chatting a young boy who looked about ten years of age came up to the table and said, *"Excuse me Mr. Australia, I just wanted to thank you for talking to us last night and wanted to tell you I am just like you"*. It actually took me time to process his words and before I could reply to him, he was gone. I said to the doctor: "Did that just happen?" and he replied, "Isn't that wonderful". After everything that I had experienced for the previous five days this stood out as the most amazing moment I had experienced. To know that I had made an impact on a young boy was as pivotal to me as the 2014 meeting at the Melbourne Zoo when I first met Christi, and learnt I wasn't alone with IA anymore.

The conference was fast coming to a close and despite the sadness of the imminent departures I realised the transformations that had occurred to me. I was also about to have one more experience that would underline my new confidence. On the last evening while I was standing by myself for a moment a lady asked if she could get a photo with me. She thanked me for my presentation the night before and explained how she and her husband had bought their grandson to the conference. She suggested that she had learned so much from my presentation that they could relate it to their 8-year-old grandson. I was very humbled that they had approached me and it was a special moment once again hearing that I may have had an impact.

Later I found Chelsea and we spoke our farewells as she was leaving very early the next morning. It was very emotional for both of us as we had spent so much time together over these intense four days. I knew that if it hadn't been for her I could have easily surrendered to my mental vulnerability and hidden away in my room many times during the conference. I owed her so much.

As I settled into my seat on the plane for my 7-day holiday in New York I reflected on what the past seven days had meant to me. I realized that my life had changed and I was now a different person. I actually felt a sense of belonging with a group of peers and that I was indeed an equal to everyone else. It was an empowering emotion and to my surprise it continued throughout the next few days.

It might have taken me 52 years, 2 months and 9 days but I was finally free in my mind, from an IA perspective. I still would have to live with the day to day physical and emotional consequences, but I was not going to make excuses for myself or allow people to use my disability against me. I had the greatest validation I could ever receive, being surrounding by my equals and embraced so enthusiastically by people who truly understand my life.

I was free of the self-imposed burden and recognized that I was responsible for the choices I made to keep my condition secret. It was exciting to feel this way and I allowed myself to think that I was going to land in New York City 11 years later than my fitful first trip and be a totally different man in so many ways.

What better way to express how proud I was to be living with IA than to wear my new T-Shirt in the most famous spot in the world: Times Square, NYC.

As the plane landed at JFK Airport, I played the song *Empire State of Mind* by Alicia Keys (her dedication to New York). As the plane landed with that song playing I wore a massive smile. The new Greg was in NYC and couldn't wait to stand in the middle of Times Square proudly displaying that he was part of the PTN community.

I had a wonderful week in New York City and reveled in the glory and freedom of what I had achieved over the last fortnight.

And there was more to come.

Chapter 16 – Triumph and Purpose

Because of my meeting with Mr. Kelly and Dr Sebastian King at the RCH in April 2016, I had struck up a rapport with Dr. King and had met him a few times subsequently to discuss my life with IA. As his specialty was treating patients with Anorectal Malformations and he had not met any adult ARM patients until I came along, I gave him a perspective which was evidently rare for any paediatric colorectal surgeons. My passion since I started my advocacy work was the crucial need of transition programs. This was an area in which he was very interested and he acknowledged had been totally overlooked in the past.

I had already booked to go to Orlando for the PTN Conference and I asked Dr. King if he could cast his eye over the presentation I was preparing. At that meeting he advised me that he was holding a paediatric colorectal conference at the hospital in October and asked if I would be interested in giving a similar presentation to the medical attendees. I agreed immediately and left the meeting feeling totally energized.

After I had returned from my trip to the USA and met again with Dr King I asked if he could invite Dr Kelly to attend, as it would be wonderful for me to pay tribute to him in front of his peers. Dr King advised he would gladly invite him.

On the 19th October 2016, I had the surreal and wonderful experience of catching up with my old doctor, Dr Dammery. It was the first time I had seen him since he had retired eight years earlier. I told him I decided to seek him out to let him know how far I had come since our last consultation. The dialogue felt more adult to adult and it was a joy to hear his recollections and perspective. I desperately felt the need to let him know that my recent successes had so much been due to his support. To my delight, he told me that he was very proud of me revealing my secret. He knew all too well how it had affected me throughout my life. He told me that I had help educate him as we jointly learnt strategies that enabled me to face my reality.

I told him I had two surgeries performed by Professor Polglase and he was pleased I was still seeing him. He disclosed that when I had first seen Professor Polglase, he had received correspondence from him in which Professor Polglase had told him he was limited in what he could do for me surgically due to my unique condition. That was personally validating (as it correlated with my experiences) but it clearly had impacted Dr. Dammery more. He advised me that he didn't tell me because he knew it would be demoralising for me at that time of my life. It reaffirmed my love for this warm and generous man and what he had done for me. We went on to discuss the form of PTSD I had endured due to all the invasive procedures and he agreed absolutely.

I shared my PowerPoint presentation with him that I was scheduled to present at the Royal Children's Hospital Paediatric Colorectal Conference the next day, and he thanked me and endorsed each slide. To get this recognition meant so much and gave me added confidence for the next day.

I thought I had reached a highlight of my life when I was at the PTN Conference meeting people just like me, but the 20th October 2016 was something even more stabilising. This presentation, in front of over 60 members of the medical fraternity from Australia and overseas, was most affirming and emotional. My Paediatric Surgeon for over 10 years when I was a child, Mr. Justin Kelly, was in attendance. It had been 32 years since I was a patient of his and I was delighted to be able to thank him publicly. It was very emotional for me as everyone joined with me in recognising him and applauding him. I'm not ashamed to say I had a tear in my eye and took me a moment to compose myself and continue the presentation.

My presentation went for 25 minutes and I received a wonderful reception which was very humbling. We then had a Q and A discussion with the attendees, and I was really taken aback by one of the woman attendees. She was a nurse named Ashley who had travelled with Dr. Levitt and 3 other colleagues from the Nationwide Children's Hospital, Columbus Ohio, which is recognised as one the preeminent Paediatric Colorectal Hospitals in the USA.

Ashley was very emotional as she spoke about how my presentation had impacted on her, and it was very satisfying to me that someone with such experience with kids with IA was so positive with the message I was trying to convey. A few days later I emailed Ashley thanking her for her kind words, and she replied quickly.

Hi Greg,

Thank you for your kind words. Your presentation was more powerful than anything else presented at the course. You're already helping to change the world of ARM. Your story is meant to be shared and there is such value in your words, experiences and journey. My life is forever impacted from hearing your story and I know I wasn't the only person in the room that felt that way. I hope you continue to use whatever platform you are given to share your story and empower kiddos around the world. Remember, YOU are more than your diagnosis, it doesn't define you. Can you please send me the poem you shared? I would love to share it with our team. Thank you again for your vulnerability and transparency.

Thank you,

Ashley RN, BSN
Center for Colorectal and Pelvic Reconstruction
Nationwide Children's Hospital
Columbus. OH USA 43205

I had many people come up to me afterwards and thank me personally for my presentation, but the best moment was when Mr. Kelly shook my hand and said Greg, you are my hero. Coming from him, it was the greatest tribute that anyone could give me. Within 24 hours, I had received plaudits from two of the greatest influences of my life, Dr Dammery and Dr Kelly. It didn't get any better than this for me.

The next day I received an email from Dr Mike O'Brien, who is the Head of Paediatric Urology/Chief of Surgery at the Royal Children's Hospital who was present for my presentation. I was incredibly humbled by Dr O'Brien's email. I excitedly showed my parents and they were even more delighted. They knew what the RCH had meant to me, and to receive such glowing praise was overwhelming. I felt like I had now completed the full circle and was able to repay the RCH and my parents.

I had barely come down from the high of the RCH presentation, before I was again spreading my wings with my work as an IA advocate. In September, I had read about an upcoming conference in Paris called the European Paediatric Colorectal & Pelvic Reconstruction Symposium.

I thought at the time how great it was that so many specialists from across the world were coming together to help share their practices and information. As well I noted that some of the prime surgeons connected to the conference were people I had met at the PTN Conference in Orlando. I was hoping that some of the issues that were raised by me and the other adults in Orlando would be raised by the Doctors/Nurses who would be attending this very large conference.

My first thought was how incredible would it be for me to attend this symposium, but that was only a dream. But the dream soon became a possibility when on 1st October I had a big win on a bet I had on the AFL Premiership. Somehow the gods had aligned to pay my way to Paris. This financial windfall was perfect opportunity for me to travel to the United Kingdom and catch up with two very close IA friends who had been an incredible support for me over the previous few years: Chrissy, who lived three hours west of London, and Rebecca who lived an hour east of London.

My main aim was to attend the Paris symposium for a day and to meet some more surgeons and nurses as I had at the Orlando Conference. That link would have helped us greatly in building up a network of specialists for our IA adult group which now stretched around the globe.

Again, by mad coincidence the network of surgeons I had met publicised me to the Paris organisers and next thing I was listed as a guest speaker.

I went ahead and booked my flights and accommodation in London which allowed me the flexibility to attend the conference. I prepared a modified PowerPoint presentation based on the one I had done at the RCH Conference, with subtle changes making it more generic. The message I wanted to convey was the patient experience and the effects on individuals from a physical and mental health perspective.

I left for my flight to London in early November and spent some wonderful time with close friend Chrissy in her hometown. I then met with other friends, Rebecca and her family and Bec and her son Eric. Both were very special periods for me.

On the 14th November, I was on board the Eurostar train which would take me the 2 ½ hour trip to Paris. I arrived at the Gare du Nord train station in Paris and organised a taxi to my hotel which was only a five-minute walk from the conference centre. I then went for a walk as I had a couple of hours spare, but unfortunately had a "bowel accident" and had to short cut my walk and do the all too familiar "walk of shame" back to the hotel.

I sorted myself out and composed myself before I headed to the conference. As soon as I disembarked the elevator onto the floor of the symposium I was delighted to see the familiar faces of Dr. Levitt and Dr. Dickie. As soon as Dr. Levitt saw me he welcomed me and thanked me for coming all the way to do give my presentation. He pulled me aside and confirmed that I shouldn't hold back because he felt the participants needed to hear my truths. To get his imprimatur was very important and it gave me the confidence that what I was about to deliver was appropriate.

I was then introduced to the organiser, Prof. Sarnacki who welcomed me very enthusiastically and thanked me for coming. She introduced me to a guy name Michel who was from the Netherlands. He was an IA Adult and to my pleasant surprise he was also there to give a patient testimony. My story is my story, but there are countless other adults who have had to deal with living with IA, so the more visibility we can provide to the paediatric colorectal fraternity in my opinion can only be of positive benefit.

As I was sitting there awaiting my turn to give my presentation I didn't feel at all anxious, it was pure excitement and anticipation. Part of me was feeling that I had lived my whole life just for this moment. I knew I wasn't just doing it for myself, but I felt very strongly that I was doing it for IA kids and adults all over the world. I was their voice today, and I was determined to make sure it was conveyed in a clear and succinct way. As an overwhelming majority of the medical professionals in attendance were involved in only Paediatric care, I felt it was important that they hear the truth and realities from someone who has lived the physical and emotional IA ride for 53 years.

I gave my 20-minute PowerPoint Presentation and speech to just over 250 surgeons, doctors and nurses. I included a story about a "bowel accident" I had just two hours earlier after arriving in Paris, so it was a raw and real-life situation I could share and re-enforced that IA was not just a paediatric issue.

The response was overwhelming. To my absolute shock, once I finished my presentation with "My Imperforate Life" poem, the whole audience started to applaud loudly and then turned this into a standing ovation for over a minute.

I couldn't believe what was happening. In shock, I took my iPhone out of my pocket and took a photo of the audience. They must have thought I was being extremely self-indulgent, but all I wanted was to capture that moment in time because I hadn't experienced anything like this in my life and I wanted to have a tangible memory. To be accepted and lauded by such luminaires of the paediatric colorectal fraternity was an incredible experience.

After the session, Michel and I had many people come up to us to congratulate us on our presentations. What was very obvious to both of us as we watched each other's presentations were the stark similarities of our experiences and battles, physically and emotionally. We both agreed that it was a perfect scenario for the attendees, as they had just witnessed two IA adults from different ends of the world and subjected to totally different medical practices, demonstrate mirrored lives.

I left Paris the next day and while sitting alone on the Eurostar travelling to London, I could but reflect on the last four months and what I had experienced. From the depths of the darkest depression this parochial boy from the suburbs of Melbourne had travelled to Orlando for a PTN Conference, celebrated in New York, been feted in London and now in Paris. I had been fortunate to meet other IA adults, IA kids and their parents, and establish a personal connection with leading paediatric colorectal surgeons from across the world. I was assisting by raising IA awareness and providing advocacy and support to the IA online community. I couldn't help but think that even though I have considered myself a failure ever since I had to accept a Disability Support Pension six year ago, maybe things do happen for a reason. The failure of my mental health and the stigma endured for over 53 years was now the catalyst for generating change.

I was between London and Paris and it appeared to me, that maybe, just maybe, I could allow myself to feel confident that I am on the same level as others. It had been a long journey.

But there was also a sense of sadness, even though I have come so far over the last few years. I was on that train by myself, and not being able to share this "triumph" with someone special, as I still have a long way to go to convince myself I'm worthy of a personal relationship. After my marriage ended I was convinced no woman would ever want to love me again, due to my array of issues. I wrestle with the unfortunate realization that I may grow old alone, it's sad but it's my reality.

I know I need to pick my battles when it comes to my health. Like the others that have become my friends I have no choice when it comes to a daily IA battle. We also must contend with mental health challenges as well. Even though having a loving relationship is a precious goal, I just can't bring myself to take on that extra crusade just yet.

When I got home it took me a few months to recover mentally and physically from my amazing trips to USA, London and Paris but in April 2017, my life took another unexpected turn, but this was a continuation of my recent positive experiences and it is not a surprise it involved my beloved North Melbourne Football club.

It evolved from a chance meeting in October 2015, when I was attending the annual Syd Barker Medal night (North Melbourne Best & Fairest). This is my one compulsory social event each year and I have attended the celebration for the last 20 plus years with dad. This night I was approached by a couple of staff members wishing to discuss a project that the club was considering. The club wanted to honor its nearly 150-year history by creating a "wall" of images and photos which would be printed on "tiles" and attached to the clubs building.

With my intimate and vast knowledge of the club, they asked if I would be interested in participating in the project. It was an amazing opportunity to do something purposeful and to indulge my greatest passion: the club's history.

I spent the next 4-5 months sourcing as many images and photos as I could by utilising any avenue open to me. I wanted to ensure that all of the players and other people who have contributed to the club's rich history were identified by an image on the "wall".

By the time I had completed the project I had collated over 1000 images and collaborated with the club's graphic department guys who were tasked with putting the images on the computer together as a timeline. The result of having the club honor its history for all to see on the walls of the building has been an amazing success, and I'm proud I was able to play my part. Once again, when I needed a purpose, the NMFC came to my rescue!

With my role in assisting with the wall and then my trips overseas doing my presentations and advocacy work, I started to slowly recapture the one thing that I had been missing since I left work in 2010, and that was a feeling of confidence in myself.

Then in April 2017, I visited the club and had a casual chat with my old manager and he mentioned that there was a void in the "history/ heritage" side of the club internally. After subsequent discussion with him and my doctors we made the decision that I would put my "toe in the water" again. So, in early May 2017, practically seven years to the day I walked out a totally broken man I walked back into the building as the happiest "volunteer" you have ever seen. I was now working 3-4 hours for two days a week.

I had only been back at NMFC for a couple of weeks when I was approached to "run my eye over" a book that was being written on the history of the club called "The Shinboners". I spent the next ten days liaising with the publisher of the book and assisting in identifying players/people featured in the book and it was a pleasure to assist where I could.

The publisher sent me the final draft before it headed to the printers for release in August 2017. There was a short paragraph acknowledging those who assisted with the production of the book. To my absolute surprise, part of the paragraph read:

"The Slattery Media Group is grateful for the support of the club in total, but in particular, Greg Ryan, whose knowledge of things Kangaroo is without peer".

To say I was shocked was an understatement, but I really appreciated the support for my contribution.

I would not have got to this stage without the mentoring of my doctors, friends and family. Without mum and dad, literally I would not have survived. But fortunately, now I see the future through the eyes of my nephews.

They are a gift to us all from my brother Brad and his lovely wife Peta. Our family has been blessed with a future through their two incredible sons, Archer and Jack. They give us all more pleasure than I could believe.

The two most loving words I hear in my life now are simple ones. The words "Uncle Greg" remind me of how fortunate a life I have really had.

And that is no secret.

Post Scripts

Post Script 1: A Dedication

There have been so many memorable moments, both happy and sad for me since the first edition of the book was released, but nothing affected me more than when I "met" one of my "little IA brothers", whose name was Max Finnigan, from England.

I formed a great friendship with Max's mum Cassie when she contacted me in August 2018, regarding purchasing a copy. She had wanted to gain 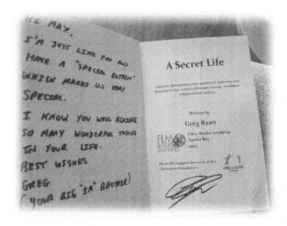 more knowledge of the challenges her then 14-month-old little "warrior" would face as he grew. We had a wonderful initial chat and I posted a book to her a day later with a special message that I like to write inside the cover for the child to let them know they aren't alone.

Cassie and her husband Jon, both read the book and Cassie and I began the first of many chats regarding her passion for raising awareness of IA/ARM in the U.K. I reported how our ONE in 5000 Foundation had recently conducted a "IA/ARM Education Seminar" in conjunction with Assoc. Prof. Sebastian King from the Royal Children's Hospital Melbourne.

The seminar was based on our A.I.M.S. which is an acronym for the vision of the foundation. Our target is increased global AWARENESS; more INFORMATION; better MEDICAL resources & improved emotional and mental SUPPORT for survivors. We based our seminar on having a session on each aspect of our vision. We posted the agenda two weeks prior to the seminar on our Facebook page, and within 24 hours a post appeared on our timeline from Cassie:

"If only we lived in Australia. Hopefully one day, it'll come to the UK. What a brilliant, brilliant thing. Greg, thank you!"

When the seminar began, we logged on to Facebook and began a "Facebook Live" broadcast for anyone who wanted to view what was happening. Even though it was very late in England, Cassie was one of the first people to "join" the broadcast, such was her thirst for education and information to help Max. She posted a comment "Well done Greg, watching from U.K."

I was really pleased with the seminar and the response from all who attended was overwhelmingly positive. I should have been on a "high" because of the success of the seminar, but I felt the absolute opposite and felt like I was "on the edge" once again as

I was physically and mentally exhausted by the end of it. I was still recovering from my latest surgery just a month prior performed by Prof. Polglase which involved repairing two "rectal mucosa prolapses", and the recovery was very difficult.

So, I kept a low profile and didn't talk to hardly anyone online, but late on the evening of Wednesday 28th November I had a look through Facebook. Shocked to the core I read the following post by Cassie and Jon:

"Our beautiful warrior Max was suddenly taken from us yesterday morning. Words cannot describe the pain and emptiness we are feeling, nor how utterly amazing, funny, clever and joyful Max was. He had been through so much in his short life and to be taken so suddenly is so unfair. The world has lost one of its future stars, who is now flying high in the sky looking down on us. We are going to miss you so much my boy. Mummy, Daddy and Big Sis love you and are incredibly proud and privileged to have had 17 amazing months together. We'll see you again one day.....xxxx"

I was absolutely shattered and started to cry uncontrollably. I immediately sent Cassie a message and I tried to sleep, but all I could think of was Cassie, her family and her beautiful little boy. I awoke to a message from Cassie, we chatted briefly, and I asked if she minded if I wrote a post on Facebook in memory of Max. Cassie accepted my suggestion.

I wrote it and sent to them beforehand to ensure they were comfortable with what I wrote, which they both were and then I posted my "tribute" to Max on my personal Facebook page as well as on the ONE in 5000 Foundation page. I offered the deepest condolences of the Australian IA/ARM community to Cassie and Jon and included the words:

"R.I.P my "little IA brother" Max, you will never ever be forgotten."

The response to the post was overwhelming, and it affected the IA/ARM community worldwide greatly. Though we recognise that IA/ARM can be fatal without surgical intervention at birth, it's extremely uncommon for a child to pass once initial surgeries have taken place. Max had come through the three mandatory surgeries of initial creating the colostomy at birth, then the PSARP surgery to create the anal opening, and then the final surgery of closing the colostomy. He was thriving and a happy little boy doing everything a boy of his age would be doing, even though he had endured so much. There had been no sign of and serious medical issue at all, other than his routine of dealing with his IA/ARM.

Cassie confided in me what had happened in that horrific eleven-hour period when Max became ill and with Cassie's permission, this is the message she sent:

"At about 7.30 in the evening during bedtime he was sick. Looks like a tummy bug with vomiting and diarrhoea and so we just did what we normally do when he's had a bug. In the early hours of the morning his breathing changed a bit and so we decided to get him seen in hospital. And very quickly he became very poorly and while we were waiting for the ambulance to arrive, he stopped breathing in my arms and his heart stopped. I resuscitated him until the paramedics arrived. They tried in hospital to resuscitate him, but his heart just wasn't strong enough. So unfair and so shocked."

The comments posted in reply to the post were full of raw emotion, absolute sadness, many tears shed, but most importantly was the incredible outpouring of love and support for Cassie, Jon & Jasmine. Cassie sent me the following message in response to the post:

"I have read all the messages this morning and it has been shared so many, many times. We are so thankful to everyone. Greg, thank you for being such a wonderful support to us. It's a wonderful community to be part of. We feel very privileged"

The post-mortem subsequently ruled out any connection to his IA/ARM condition and in an incredible gesture of selflessness,

Cassie asked to post a message to everyone from her and Jon, as they wanted to allay any fears parents in our community may have had in relation to his passing and his IA/ARM condition:

"Thank you all for your kind words, prayers and love. We are going through every parent's nightmare and we are forever heart broken. Max passed away very suddenly after a very short (11 hour) illness overnight. We still don't know why and won't for some time yet but what we definitely do know is that it wasn't related to his IA/ARM whatsoever as confirmed by subsequent tests." #InMemoryOfMax

In subsequent discussions with Cassie she had asked me if I was prepared to help organise a British version of an **"IA/ARM Education Seminar"** based on the same model as the Royal Children's Hospital Melbourne activity. We were delighted to honour Max's memory, and they then asked friends and families to donate to the ONE in 5000 Foundation, to assist in making this possible.

The response has been phenomenal. After the initial request for donations to come directly through a PayPal link on the ONE in 5000 Foundation website, Cassie and Jon then decided to start a "crowdfunding" page in the U.K. which would enable funds to be donated in a more streamlined way. The heading of the page was:

"We're raising money to fund-raise for the ONE in 5000 Foundation to host an IA/ARM conference in the UK in 2019, in memory of Max Finnigan (17 months)"

They then wrote the most heart-warming and heartbreaking story in their own words detailing Max's life:

"Our beautiful boy Max was born in June 2017, weighing 10 pounds and apparently healthy. A day later our joy turned to fear as he became listless and uninterested in feeding. It transpired that he had been born with a little-known condition known as Imperforate Anus (IA), a type of Anorectal Malformation (ARM).

The incidence of this is one in 5000 births. There was no opening in Max's anus for waste to escape his system and his tummy quickly became distended. His bowel had formed a fistula with his urethra. He was rushed to surgery where he underwent an operation to form a colostomy and a mucus fistula.

Max underwent his second operation just less than three months later, which involved cutting him open from behind his testicles to his coccyx and detaching the bowel from the urethra and connecting it to a newly formed anus. This was a delicate and long operation but was a success.

A further five months later Max underwent his third operation, which involved the closure of his stoma and a nervous wait whilst he recovered. We eagerly anticipated his first poo and fortunately

159

we only had to wait a couple of days for his first pooey nappy! In the months that followed Max went from as many as twenty nappy changes a day down to about five as his bowel settled slowly.

Despite three major operations in the first eight months of his life, including one on the first day, he fought and recovered so quickly. He was the happiest, funniest and most loving baby boy who thrived. As for us, whilst we made sure Max lived a life full of fun and new experiences, we were struck by how little support there was in the IA/ARM community, including the lack of charities to raise awareness.

We learned of the ONE in 5000 Foundation, set up by an inspirational man called Greg Ryan from Australia who was born with IA and spent much of his life struggling with his "Hidden Secret" until he started sharing his experiences and helping others born with IA. He wrote a book, A Secret Life - Surviving a rare congenital condition, which we read. We vowed that Max would grow up knowing about and being proud of his condition and, hopefully, become an ambassador for ONE in 5000 and IA/ARM.

Sadly, Max suddenly passed away in November 2018 from an unrelated illness aged 17 months. We are heartbroken, empty and forever changed, but in time we are determined to ensure that Max's legacy endures and his light lives on. He really was an IA/ARM Warrior who made us proud and full of love every day.

He has already inspired the creation of a ONE in 5000 UK support group for families living with IA/ARM and the Foundation have further announced that, in Max's memory, they want to bring a conference to the UK that will bring families affected by IA together with specialists in the field from around the world.

So, if you've been inspired by our story and would like to help us make the UK conference happen, please consider donating. All money raised will go directly to the ONE in 5000 Foundation and towards raising awareness, information, medical, and support for families and professionals. Please help us keep our amazing Max's memory alive and continue his legacy.

For further information, please visit the ONE in 5000 Foundation website: www.onein5000foundation.org."

The response to the crowdfunding page was wonderful and the funds received will ensure that not only the seminar and a very special family day for the U.K. IA/ARM community will take place, but it will also ensure that awareness and understanding of our condition will be able to be shared to the wider community.

I had committed to making this seminar happen "In Memory of Max", and when I discussed with a few close friends in the UK, they all offered to volunteer their services in any way possible. We all agreed that we wanted to ensure that no extra burden placed on the Finnigan family, and it was very important I had that support from people on the ground in London to assist.

Even though circumstances surrounding the passing of Max have been so intolerable for his family and friends, the one positive the family will be able to hold on to is that he is the catalyst that will forever change the landscape of the IA/ARM community in the United Kingdom, as we spread awareness, understanding and education.

The seminar and family day are only the start, and in the first session of the seminar, Cassie and Jon will be given the opportunity to pay tribute to their beautiful son to fellow IA/ARM families and ensure his name in entrenched in the U.K. IA/ARM community forever. For my part, the best tribute I can do is promise Cassie and Jon that going forward, anytime I am given the opportunity to talk publicly or in conferences, I will mention Max Finnigan. He will be my "partner" in the ONE in 5000 Foundation forever.

Post Script 2: Impact of Publishing this Book

It's hard to describe adequately how the publishing of the 1st edition of **A Secret Life – Surviving a Rare Congenital Condition** has changed all aspects of my life since it was released in September 2017. I am delighted that the major impact of the book has been to give survivors of IA/ARM a voice in describing their needs.

My struggle and that of my family was one story of many that have been hidden and are now being heard. Our world is changing fast after many years of neglect and now there are more people coming of the shadows to discuss the impact of IA/ARM on their lives.

In the 18 months since the release, the book has been distributed to 55 countries and the response has been overwhelmingly positive. The feedback especially from IA/ARM parents has been the most important to me. I fully recognise that since I was born 54 years ago there have been many positive medical advancements, but unfortunately there is no permanent or complete "fix" and hence the physical and emotional challenges children face today are very similar to those I faced. It is here that the book has given many families a long-term perspective.

One of the flow on effects of the book has been that parents have been able to share it with family members and school teachers, as an educational tool, and it helped them explain what their child was experiencing. This has given parents the chance to validate their challenges.

The most surprising outcome for me has been the response from the paediatric colorectal/urological professionals. I was aware that my presentations at conferences over the last few years had an influence. However, the response to the book was very satisfying and many doctors better recognized the services that are needed for a holistic solution.

Clearly my story is helping those Doctors better appreciate the emotional needs of the IA/ARM community and giving a greater and much needed focus to these issues.

Much to my delight and surprise, once the book was published, Dr Marc Levitt who had graciously written the foreword for the first edition of the book contacted me to advise that on behalf of Nationwide Children's Hospital he wanted to order 300 books to distribute to the attendees of the "Paediatric Colorectal, Motility & Pelvic Reconstruction Conference" to be hosted at Nationwide Children's Hospital in Columbus, Ohio.

We sourced a printer in the USA to get the books produced and I travelled to Columbus for the conference and presented a short reading of the book. I had many discussions with medical professionals in attendance and established a great network which I knew could be utilised to help others in the IA/ARM community.

Samples of the responses include highly regarded surgeons like Dr Donald Shaul who wrote:

"Hi Greg,

I wanted to send you a short note to let you know that I have finished reading the book that you gave me at the Colorectal Conference at Nationwide CH. I appreciate your willingness to share the ups and downs of your courageous journey with us. It is interesting to read your story because I have met both Nate Myers and Justin Kelly at past conferences, so I feel that connection to you as well.

Anyway, as a result of reading your story, we will certainly put more emphasis on the mental health needs of our little patients and their families.

All the best to you until we meet again,

Don Shaul
Regional Chief of Pediatric Surgery
Kaiser Permanente, Los Angeles Medical Center

Soon after Dr Shaul's contact I received an email from Dr Alberto Pena. Dr Pena is recognised worldwide as the man who revolutionised the treatment of IA/ARM patients when he introduced a new surgical technique in 1980 which was called the PSARP (Posterior Sagittal Anorectoplasty). He wrote:

Dear Mr. Greg Ryan,

I just finished reading your very inspirational book "A Secret Life". First of all, please accept my sincere admiration and respect! Also, please transmit my feeling to your parents, who played a crucial role in your long and painful journey. As you can imagine, I had the privilege to learn and be part of many similar stories. It has been my experience that patients born with bad prognosis type of anorectal malformations and their parents, go through different suffering stages, beginning with the shock feeling of learning that their beloved newborn baby has no anus!!. Something that most people never heard about. Later on, sometimes they become angry and ask themselves "why me?" Subsequently, parents and children go through the extremely painful path represented by the confrontation with our rather cruel society, attending school, having embarrassing "accidents" and all those terrible events that you narrated so well in your book.

Eventually, many parents and patients find a MEANING to all their pain and suffering. I have the feeling after reading your book that you already reached that point. It sounds like you find a MEANING. This, I think, started when you decided to share your story with others. After your trip to Orlando, after you met all those teenagers, after you met that child who called you "Mr. Australia" you realized that your story, your presence, your words, your experience meant a lot for many, perhaps thousands of other human beings.

Just consider this: imagine that when you were 10 yrs. old, you met an adult who called you and said: "Greg, I know exactly how you feel, I have been there and I am here to help you".

I am sure that now you know that you have a mission, a beautiful one. You can certainly alleviate the suffering of hundreds of children. You just had a little sample of your mission in Orlando. Congratulations. I look forward to hear more about your work for the benefit of children born with anorectal malformations and their parents.

In your message, you mentioned that you would like to know my opinion from the medical point of view. Here is what I think:

From the time that you were born until know, we have learned a lot about anorectal malformations, its natural history, its prognosis and the management of the associated malformations. ....In 1969, 70 and 71, I trained at Boston Children's Hospital. As a coincidence, Dr. Justin Kelly was a Fellow also in 1969 and 1970. We become good friends. Even when he was a Fellow, he came to Boston as an emissary of Dr. Douglas Stephens who was a creative research-oriented type of pediatric Surgeon, who published his new ideas about the treatment of these malformations. Consequently, Dr. Kelly gave several lectures to all the surgical staff at Boston Children's. All, of us learned from him the "Stephen's approach"

In January 1972 I went back to Mexico and became Chief of Surgery of the National Institute of Pediatrics. For 8 years I operated many cases of anorectal malformations, following Dr. Stephens recommendations. However, Dr. Stephen's approach included some blind manoeuvres and therefore, I gradually modified his technique. Finally, on August 10 of 1980 I performed the first Posterior Sagittal AnorectoPlasty (PSARP). With the new approach we could see directly the intrinsic anatomy of the lower end of the rectum and its relationship with the most critical portion of the male anatomy, including prostate, seminal vesicles, vas deferens and the nerves that control penile erection. The functional results (bowel and urinary control) obtained with the new approach were significantly better. However, very soon I realized that anorectal malformations are represented by a wide spectrum of defects. In the "good" side of the spectrum we operate and our patients and they have bowel and urinary control. In the "bad" side of the spectrum, the patients will never gain bowel control and sometimes they also have urinary incontinence. They are born with serious anatomic deficiencies, they do not have the necessary elements to achieve continence and so far, we do not know how to cure them.

Since 1980 and until today, I have done over 3000 cases and have learned many lessons that allowed us to make significant advances in the management of anorectal malformations, although we have a long way to go. I have been trying to follow all my patients to adult life. Based on the information collected during all these years, we can now predict the future of the babies, in a fairly accurate way.

If a baby like you is born today, we use the first 24 hrs. of his life to do very important diagnostic studies which will allow to determine the functional prognosis of the baby. In other words, we believe that it is extremely important to determine the future prognosis, in order to allow the parents to adjust their expectations, all this to avoid the saga that your parents went through. The studies are:

- *X-ray of the sacrum (lowest part of our spine).*
- *Kidney ultrasound*
- *Spinal ultrasound.*

The sacrum is extremely important. An absent sacrum means no chances of having bowel control. Yet the sacrum may be partially developed. We developed an objective way to quantify the quality of the sacrum and were able to correlate with the chances to have bowel control. We call that "Sacral ratio". I was surprised that you did not mention the word "sacrum" in your book.

Approximately fifty percent of all patients born with anorectal malformation have a kidney problem; a simple kidney ultrasound allows us to rule out this important associated defect.

Approximately 25 % of all patients born with anorectal malformation also have a condition called "Tethered Cord". The presence of this defect affects to some degree the bowel function and even more the urinary function.

After these studies have been done, the baby he will receive a colostomy, which will keep him in the hospital about 3-4 days. Four to eight weeks after, we will do a study called distal colostogram, which is the best diagnostic test in the management of anorectal malformations. That study will allow us to know the precise anatomic diagnosis. Usually, about one or two months after birth the baby undergoes the repair of his malformation, called PSARP, which keeps him 48 hrs. in the hospital. I have learned that approximately 10 % of the male cases need an abdominal operation in addition to the PSARP, in order to reach a rectum located very high in the pelvis.

Two weeks after the main repair, I show the parents how to do anal dilatations. Once the parents reach the desired anal calibre (usually two months after the PSARP), the colostomy is closed; this is a procedure that takes about two hours and the baby stays in the hospital for 3-4 days.

Once the colostomy is closed, we concentrate in avoiding constipation and being sure that we give the right amount of laxatives to be sure that the baby empties the colon completely every day, as radiologically demonstrated. We have learned that every patient needs a different amount of laxative and we must determine the laxative requirement by trial and error. We have also learned that when constipation is not treated properly, the patient suffers from fecal impaction, which interferes with bowel control. In other words, patients born with "good prognosis" type of malformations, and do not receive adequate treatment for constipation, will never become toilet trained. When patient receive the right amount of laxatives, there is no need for enemas.

From the time the colostomy is closed, and until the age of bowel control (2 ½ to 3 years of age), the patient uses diapers and receives laxatives. By the age of 2 ½ or 3 yrs. Most normal babies become toilet trained and that is when the parents decide to send them to school. If the patient belongs to the "good prognosis group" he/she will become toilet trained. On the other hand, if the baby belongs to the "poor prognosis group", we offer the parents our "Bowel Management Program", consisting in the use of enemas, which will keep the patients COMPLETELY clean of stool for 24 hours. It sounds to me like the way you were receiving enemas was to treat episodes of fecal impaction. You and your parents were literally "paying the price" of having enemas and not receiving the benefit of the enemas. The principles of our Bowel Management Program are:

- Every human being has a different size and motility of the colon and therefore needs a specially designed enema. (there are many types of enemas)
- The only way to objectively know if an enema cleaned the colon is by taking an abdominal X-ray film
- It takes us one week to determine, by trial and error, taking daily X-ray films the volume and ingredients of an enema.

- *We oppose to send children suffering from fecal incontinence, to school. We believe that children can go to school only when we can guarantee that they will remain completely clean in their underwear.*
- *When the Bowel Management Program is followed correctly, there not must be episodes of fecal impaction and visits to the emergency room.*
- *When the patients suffer from serious anatomic deficiencies, we can anticipate that the bowel management must be followed for life. Under those circumstances, when the child is 7yrs old or older, we offer the family the operation called Malone procedure (continent appendicostomy), which avoids rectal enemas and allows the patient to become independent.*
- *Painful enemas happen when something is not done right or in patients who have aversion to any kind of rectal manoeuvres due to severe traumas inflicted during their early lives. (Painful dilatations, severe diaper rash)*
- *Bowel Management Programs as described here, did not exist at a time when you were treated; enemas were given "when necessary", usually to fecally disimpact a child.*

Concerning the occurrence of torsion of the testicle and orchioepididimytis. We have learned that orchioepididimytis is a serious condition which requires a full urologic evaluation. It is usually secondary to a chronic urinary tract infection, some sort of reflux of urine into the vas deferens, anatomic abnormalities of the vas deferens connecting abnormally to the bladder or to a ureter. During the last 33 years, I have not heard of a case of torsion of the testicle in patients with anorectal malformations. However, many of my patients have been operated with the wrong diagnosis of torsion of the testicle, only to find that actually the patient had an orchioepididimytis.

Concerning genitalia associated defects, in our series, 8 % of the male patients have a condition called hypospadias. From your description, it sound like perhaps you suffer from a form of hypospadias. I cannot expand more to discuss sexual function. We see many adult patients coming to us complaining of sexual problems. To study them, we order an MRI study of their pelvis, a voiding cyst urethrogram and a cystoscopy. With those studies we found a variety of problems including posterior urethral diverticulum's (piece of bowel left attached to the urethra), damaged prostate, urethral strictures and ejaculatory ducts connected to the bladder, which explains in some cases the reason why the patient did not ejaculate externally.

I hope I did not confuse you with all this information. If you have questions, do not hesitate to ask me.

Again, I congratulate you for your strength and endurance. I sincerely hope that you continue using your experience to benefit many children and parents of the world.

Best wishes

Alberto Peña, MD, FAAP, FACS, FRCS |Ponzio Family Chair for Colorectal Pediatric Surgery |Director, International Center for Colorectal Care| Children's Hospital Colorado|Professor of Surgery University of Colorado

I believe this information is incredibly educational and informative, but most importantly it gives such a wonderful insight into the role Dr Pena has taken in supporting the survivor and the families. Recently I also received an email from Dr Andrea Bischoff saying:

"Dear Greg,

Yesterday I was finally able to read your book from beginning to end without any interruption! The book has been living in the table next to my bed for a long time and have gone with me for several trips abroad... but it meant so much to me that I really wanted to be fully concentrated to read it, and that was the reason why it took me so long. What coincidence that I read it on World Mental Health Day!

I enjoyed very much. You were very open on how the bowel accidents impacted you and how enemas also had a negative impact on you. I was wondering if after talking to so many patients with imperforate anus if you have met others that had a different experience?

I truly wish that you and all our patients could see and feel that love does not care about perfection, because nobody is perfect. I usually tell my patients to think about someone that they love deeply, then I ask them to imagine that for the first time I am letting them know that this person doesn't have the left foot, he/she has a prosthetic foot. Would that change the love that they feel? So far, everybody has answered me with a categorical no. With that story I try to convey the message that when somebody loves you, the "imperforate anus" will not make a difference.

I think you have had phenomenal achievements in your life and I look forward to continue to hear from them.

Yesterday I also saw the documentary about Mr. Rogers – Won't you be my neighbor? I did not grow up in the United States but I was impressed how good he was with kids and what great message he was able to convey to children that they were loved and special just the way they were.

Here, at Children's Hospital Colorado, we are trying to provide, to the best of our capacity, psychological support for all patients in the hope that we better address difficult times.

Thanks for writing the book and thanks for all your efforts.

Andrea

Andrea Bischoff, MD | Assistant Director, International Center for Colorectal and Urogenital Care| Children's Hospital Colorado Associate Professor of Surgery University of Colorado"

In August 2017, my wonderful friend Chelsea Mullins (pictured) and I were invited by Dr Pena & Dr Bischoff to be presenters in a Colorectal Patient/Family Web Meeting that is broadcast all over

the world. They were very keen for people in the community to hear from adults with the "lived patient experience". We were also able to join the dialogue discussing the impact of the "Adults living with IA" Facebook support group and the impact the group had on the adults who until then felt so alone.

Chelsea and I gave a PowerPoint presentation and took turns in discussing each slide. It was a wonderful opportunity, but most importantly it was a sign of the intense commitment that Dr Pena & Dr Bischoff had towards the "transitional care" program they had initiated.

In November 2018, Chelsea and I received an email from Dr Bischoff inviting us both to present a patient testimony at the "The Surgical Treatment of Colorectal Problems in Children" course to be held at Children's Hospital Colorado April 10-12, 2019. Dr Bischoff advised that the main purpose would be to motivate the doctors to continually improve the quality of life of colorectal patients.

In the advertising material for the registration for medical professionals, the following quote is included:

"NEW to the course will be a session about #TransitionofCare in colorectal, we will expand on the session addressing #MentalHealth and social needs for colorectal patients, and what we are most excited about it: we will start each day with a patient testimony, to remind everyone about the reason why we are all in this course."

This is a stunning development for survivors and we consider this a very special honour and an acknowledgment of our advocacy work.

Post Script 3: Adults Gaining Voice

In July 2018, I was fortunate to return to the USA to attend the bi-annual Pull-Thru Network conference, this time in Phoenix, Arizona. This was very special to me because not only was I getting to meet all the marvelous people I met in Orlando 2016, but I had come into contact with many more families due to the release of the book. I had many conversations online with parents who had purchased the book, but the most wonderful thing was that so many parents had sent me a photo of their IA/ARM child holding a copy of the book, to me that was priceless.

What made the trip even more special was that I was joined by a lovely friend of mine, Anja, who was a 21-year-old IA/ARM woman from Brisbane, Australia. We had met in early 2018 through an online support group and we immediately struck up a close and supportive bond. The most pleasing thing for her was that she finally had met someone else who could understand what she had endured due to her VACTERL condition. I also invited her to come to Melbourne for two meetings we had in regard to the ONE in 5000 Foundation, and her perspective was invaluable. When I advised her that I was attending the PTN conference, she decided she had to be there and we organised to fly over from our respective states.

It was a very special moment for me to sit in the audience when she and another wonderful IA/ARM woman, Angelea from the USA, both give presentations to the attendees at the conference, just like Chelsea, Alan and I had in Orlando in 2016. I was a very proud "big brother" and I know it was a life-changing event for Anja, as it was for me earlier and I know she will be a wonderful role-model and advocate for young IA/ARM girls around the world.

Even though travelling such a long distance and the immense fear of "accidents" on the plane comes at a cost physically and mentally, the unbridled joy I get when I'm around my "IA/ARM family" cannot be measured. To get to see the smiles of beautiful, courageous young IA/ARM boys like Nico, Levi, Tyler, Theo, Caleb, Noah and Nikolas and to get a photo with them is incredibly satisfying and better for me than any medication I get prescribed. I'm so glad they know they aren't alone.

A pleasing aspect of this conference was that there were over 20 adults attending (compared to six in 2016), which really was particularly significant in the session titled: "PTN Adults Q & A with Doctors". There was extremely open and honest dialogue with a focus on the massive psychological toll, lack of transitional care programs and lack of awareness of adult colorectal clinicians relating to IA/ARM.

The doctors present acknowledged and valued the issues raised and it was mentioned by more than one doctor, that they had found the adult session the most productive. Due to such a large and diverse group of adults with age spans from 18 to 60, they were learning incredibly important aspects of what living with IA/ARM can be like, which in turn assists their treatment and care of children.

On the first afternoon of the conference Anja and I attended a session called "Psychosocial Needs of Parenting a Medically Complex Child", as one of my greatest passions is advocating for greater mental health awareness for IA/ARM kids. The session was being conducted by Dr Laura Judd-Glossy, who is a Paediatric Psychologist at Children's Hospital Colorado who works very closely with Dr Pena and Dr Bischoff.

During the session, there was a question by one of the parents regarding "now her 5-year-old son has developed an issue with wanting to control everything at home". After Dr Judd-Glossy, gave her opinion, I raised my hand to contribute to the conversation.

I introduced myself as "Greg, from Australia and I'm a PTN adult", and immediately Dr Judd-Glossy said "are you the Greg who wrote the book?", to which I sheepishly replied "yeah". I addressed the mum who asked the question and stated that in my case, I live life trying to "control my environment", because I have never been able to "control my bowels". Immediately she nodded her head and said "OMG I hadn't thought of it that way". After the session, I spoke with Dr Judd-Glossy about the psychological impacts of living with IA/ARM. We discussed the possibility of Children's Hospital Colorado initiating a formal "survey" which we would publish in the "Adults living with IA" group.

I advised her that I had conducted a poll recently in the group asking for a YES or NO to the following question: "Have you had to seek medical help for any mental health issues?"

The result was that 95% of respondents clicked YES.

This is a damning statistic, but not surprising at all to those adults who have joined our group, which now has grown to just under 250 people from around the world. When I advised Dr Judd-Glossy of this statistic, she advised that she would discuss with Dr Bischoff on her return.

It was extremely pleasing to receive an email from Dr Bischoff and Dr Judd-Glossy in January 2019 to advise that the "survey" was now ready to be shared to the "adult group". This is the message from Dr Judd-Glossy that accompanied the survey which I posted in the group:

"The International Center of Colorectal and Urogenital Care at Children's Hospital Colorado are interested in learning more about the experiences of adults with colorectal conditions, in order to provide better support to our current and future colorectal patients and their families. You are invited to participate in this survey, which will ask about your experience as an adult living with a colorectal condition. This anonymous survey will take approximately 10 to 15 minutes to complete. Please contact Laura Judd-Glossy for more information or with any questions.

Thank you so much!"

The response to the survey was immediate and positive by members in the group and there was a sense of relief and acknowledgment that everyone's voices are finally being heard after years of feeling abandoned by the medical profession.

I know this survey will make a difference to the way IA/ARM patients are cared for and treated in the future and that the results can be shared to the pediatric colorectal medical community globally.

As was mentioned by one of the doctors in the "PTN Adults Q & A with Doctors" session, he considered the "PTN adults" to be the "real experts", and it's wonderful and gratifying that our voices are finally being heard.

Post Script 4: The ONE in 5000 Foundation

The ONE in 5000 Foundation online presence has continued to grow throughout the IA/ARM worldwide. We owe many thanks to a strong and high-profile advisory board of volunteers and a resource development team consisting of a Paediatric Colorectal Surgeon; IA/ARM Adults; IA/ARM Parents; Educators and a Psychotherapist/Counsellor.

Our Foundation is registered as a Charity in Australia and as we mention elsewhere we have established our A.I.M.S. vision based on 4 measurable goals:

AWARENESS: *That every child is born into an aware community that understands the nature of Imperforate Anus (IA) / Anorectal Malformation (ARM) issues and the need for human support for each child and family members.*

INFORMATION: *That parental access be provided to comprehensive online resources, appropriate to their child's current age and the nature of this congenital condition, featuring material including but not limited to: Personal Stories (Parent; Patient; & Clinicians); Videos; Answers to Common Questions;*

Research Data & Government Support Programs.

MEDICAL: *That a network of first rate surgical and clinical care providers from a well-coordinated set of medical practitioners and mental health specialists be guaranteed.*

SUPPORT: *Mental Health supports for child, parent and family at equivalent level to any other congenital condition by providing a world best practice peer support program which links well trained IA/ARM community members with experienced peers.*

With the establishment of our A.I.M.S. we then proceeded to build a website www.onein5000foundation.org which we believe will be the major online support for the IA/ARM community worldwide.

This is the introduction message to the webpage:

"Our website serves to provide this resource by connecting all within the IA / ARM community, which includes families, adults with the lived experience, and a network of medical professionals from both the clinical and mental health perspective, who specialise in the paediatric colorectal field.

Up until recently IA and ARM have been almost completely unknown to most of the world's population. A few GPs and a group of specialist doctors and the families affected by Imperforate Anus and Anorectal Malformation know it all too well as a very difficult congenital event that influences many lives up to One in every 5000 babies born in the western world. This website aims to give these people as much information as possible to help them handle the results of this congenital event.

The website has over 30 personal stories from parents and patients from across the world and has been an invaluable resource to so many, as well as having a video section where people can view a very substantive interview with world recognised Paediatric Colorectal Surgeon. It also provides a list of IA/ARM specialist clinicians from across the globe with links to their hospitals.

The webpage is constantly being updated with "latest news" and will eventually be available in different languages. As part of the online work through the Facebook groups, which catered solely for IA/ARM Adults and Parents, we are keen to establish a greater network of clinicians across the world to add to the network which had been established through the conferences attended in the previous two years.

It became very apparent that the social networking site LinkedIn, which is specifically designed for the business community, would be the perfect vehicle to promote the ONE in 5000 Foundation and the advocacy work we had already undertaken. We have been able to create a "connection" with nearly 200 clinicians who are involved in treating paediatric colorectal patients from across the world, and it has become an invaluable resource to connect IA/ARM patients and parents to clinicians in their country.

It has also been valuable, not only to promote the work of the Foundation but also to keep updated with "medical papers" which have been written on IA/ARM on recent studies etc.

In April 2018, we were made aware of an organisation called "Global PaedSurg", after a post on LinkedIn by Dr Naomi Wright (Paediatric Surgery Registrar and PhD Fellow, King's Centre for Global Health and Health Partnerships) who was the "Principal Investigator" for "Global PaedSurg".

Dr Wright was then tasked with finding collaborators from across the world for study that would be taking place for a minimum of one month between October 2018 – April 2019 into seven congenital anomalies, for which Anorectal Malformation was included. According to their website, this is the description of their organisation:

"Global PaedSurg" is a multi-centre research collaboration of surgeons, anaesthetists and allied health professionals caring for neonates and children requiring surgery across the globe. This aims to be the first large-scale geographically comprehensive prospective cohort study on the management and outcomes of congenital anomalies in low-, middle- and high-income countries across the globe"

Naturally this peaked interest and we immediately sent a message through LinkedIn to Dr Wright, detailing our history regarding IA/ARM and our advocacy work and asked if we could be of any assistance to their research project. Within 48 hours we received the following reply from Dr Wright on LinkedIn:

Dear Greg Ryan,

Thank you very much for your message. It means a great deal to have your support and backing for this project. It would be wonderful if you could help to promote participation in the study when you are presenting around the world. I wonder also whether you could write a brief blog for our website regarding your experiences and need for research and advocacy for patients with ARM and other congenital anomalies.

In the first instance I wonder whether a quick Skype call would be useful so I can discuss the study with you in a little more detail. Next Friday would be a good day if you are free. It will probably be easiest for us to correspond on email in the future.

Kindest regards,

Naomi

The blog was written, but more importantly after the subsequent "Skype" call we had we were even more excited about how incredibly valuable this cohort study was going to be for our IA/ARM community. Dr Wright had previously been involved heavily in paediatric care in Africa, where the mortality rate for IA/ARM is much higher than in developed countries, and we knew this study was going to be so important for under developed countries, but also for our community on so many levels.

We committed to assist in any way possible and posted a link to the Global PaedSurg webpage on our Facebook pages, as well as our website. The most pleasing aspect was that we were able to put Dr Wright in contact with clinicians who we had met over the last few years. At the end of 2018, the Global PaedSurg had 1552 collaborators; 458 hospitals involved; 114 countries represented and had 881 patients as at January 2019.

It is a remarkable achievement by all those involved, and the research and data collated at the end of the study period will be of great significance. The greatest legacy is that it will save the lives of IA/ARM babies, and nothing is more important than that.

The use of Facebook has been critical to the ONE in 5000 Foundation as we have our own Facebook page @ONEin5000Foundation and we have over 700 followers as we go to print. This network has been pivotal in assisting families throughout the world due to the link with clinicians, especially in under developed countries where the patient care is under resourced and not specialised due to the complexity of IA/ARM conditions.

In November 2018, a new Facebook group was created named the "ONE in 5000 U.K. Support Group", which catered solely for the IA/ARM community throughout the United Kingdom. We had discussed this with a wonderful IA/ARM mother, Bec, with whom we had established a close friendship. With the support of her husband Colin, the group has become an instant success with approaching 150 members joining at the time of printing. A wonderful sense of belonging and community has already been created and likely to be enhanced by the London seminar.

With the success of the U.K. group, our contact in France, Jordane (an IA/ARM adult) declared that she would wish to develop a similar awareness and advocating group in her country. Our support meant in January 2019 the "ONE in 5000 France Page" was created. It is (naturally) written in French and is starting to gain traction thanks to Jordane's passion and the assistance of a wonderful IA/ARM mother, Cheryl. We know the group will continue to thrive.

With the success of the "IA/ARM Education Seminar" in Melbourne Australia, October 2018, and with a similar seminar being conducted in London UK in April 2019, it is great recognition for all the people who are involved in the ONE in 5000 Foundation.

I would also like to mention the significance of the colours chosen for our foundation logo (shown in colour on back cover of book), which are brown and yellow. We deliberately chose these two colours to emphasise and highlight that IA/ARM is related to bowel and bladder.

It's just an extra commitment that we made to lessen the stigma that has been associated with our condition for too long. Most importantly, we want to ensure that IA/ARM is accepted in the community, both medically and publicly, as a condition which should be acknowledged and accepted on the same level as the more commonly known conditions relating to the bowel and bladder, which unfortunately has not been the case in the history of IA/ARM.

With the wonderful support and encouragement from the IA/ARM community of patients, families and clinicians, we are confident we will continue to grow and stay true to our commitments.

An Afterword: Australian Football at North Melbourne – A True Love

My family will always be the most important thing in my life, but my affiliation for my football club has at many times been massively supportive, and it deserves at least a postscript. Like many people around the world I have been a fan of an elite team of sports people. As well I have had the privilege of working inside that club, getting to know its stars and the countless others that make a team strong. Given the mental health issues I have described in this book I am very conscious that without my club I may not have survived.

It's rather ironic, but the two things that I believe have defined me as a person are at opposite ends of the scale. My IA was totally a secret and I protected it with all my might. Whereas, I openly expressed my love and obsession of the North Melbourne Football Club (Kangaroos). To anyone who ever met me, be it a school class-mate, a friend, or a work colleague, the message was clear. There was no doubt that North and I were intertwined.

My paternal great-grandparents where born in North Melbourne, as were both my paternal grandparents and then my dad. The love of the club was embedded in me at birth and other than my hospital visits, my earliest memories are of North and footy. I distinctly remember being in hospital for one of my surgeries when I was a child and my parents bringing me a football record (program) from a footy game that day.

I recognise now that my love of North as a child gave me an escape from all my medical issues and allowed me to be "normal" for some of the time at least. I didn't need to hide or feel shame when I went to watch my beloved Kangaroos. I was just another face in the crowd barracking hard for my team and my heroes. This was my escape.

In 1971, my dad applied for a casual position as a Weights Coach with the club and was subsequently appointed. Dad had been a champion Weightlifter and held Australian and Commonwealth records during his career. When he retired, he believed he could offer a unique perspective regarding strength conditioning for footballers and due to his love of North, he approached North. Fortunately, the senior coach at the time identified that dad could offer specialised coaching and was the first person appointed in VFL with a weightlifting background.

What that meant for our family was that we could become a part of the inner sanctum of the club which for me as 7-year-old, and for my younger brother Brad, was a dream come true. Through dad's involvement, we were now able to see our heroes firsthand in the change rooms and when we visited training.

Two years after dad started, he became a match day trainer, which meant he was on the ground during the games tending to injured players and providing drinks and physical advice. This meant that mum would sit with the player's wives and girlfriends and consequently my parents formed great friendships. These links led to a lot of socialising, and my brother and I were now seeing our heroes as family friends.

We would go to the footy with dad, but then sit with our grandparents and uncle and aunties and go home with them while mum and dad would celebrate or commiserate with players and staff afterwards.

Never did I feel more alive as a kid than when I was at the North oval in Arden Street, which was less than a kilometre from my grandparents' home. I look back with great affection of these times as we walked home after our games with my grandparents. Always we were aware that our great-grandmother was waiting for us at the back gate.

The one regret I've always lived with regarding North happened in 1975 when I was 11 years of age. The Club won its first ever premiership cup and I was at the ground to watch the game with my grandparents. After the game, we then went back to their house but rather than going with my grandparents to celebrate with all the other success-starved, lifelong supporters at the Club, I was having a bad bowels night and was too scared to leave the house and the safety of the toilet that night. I've regretted my absence all my life, but I had no choice, my IA deciding on that night that it would remind me that it could affect my life no matter the circumstances.

Even when I started to play footy, as much as I enjoyed playing with my mates, the only thing that mattered for me was that

North won on that weekend. One of the hardest decisions I had to make in my teenage years was when I was playing in my Under 16 year. Because we played at 2 pm on a Saturday afternoon, that meant our games clashed and I wouldn't be able to watch North play. I decided to play with my mates and first thing I did after the game was find the North result.

Once I turned 18, I could finally go to night clubs and get my driver's license. The first nightclub I ever went to was the Disco at the North Melbourne Social Club which was very popular at the time. I attended every Thursday and Friday night for a few years. I even did some part-time work as a "Glass-boy" collecting empty glasses during the night and on some occasions worked on the front till collecting patron's admission monies. I loved going "down North" as we used to call it, as it was downstairs at the Social club.

When it came to my 21st Birthday celebrations, there was only one place I was ever going to have my party, and that was at the North Social Club. I felt normal when I watched North play and I felt the same when I was "down North". I was just another patron who loved the club, not the insecure person who was paranoid about his secret being revealed. It was a sad occasion when the North Disco closed when I was 22 years of age.

By early 1987, an opportunity arose for a position as Team Manager of North's Reserve Grade team. As I was always around the club and with dad's involvement, I approached the football manager at the time and made myself available. Even though I was only 22 and still immature, I felt my passion for the club and my 5-years of adult working experience were useful credentials. As well I was working at Budget Rent-A-Car which was only 1 kilometer away from the ground.

I was successful and appointed to the position and at that stage of my life, I felt it was my greatest achievement. Even though I got through school with my secret intact and was working full time under difficult circumstances at times, to get this volunteer position in the inner sanctum of my beloved club was beyond my wildest dreams. It quickly became more important to me than anything else in my life.

When I was appointed to the role at North, my dad was still weights coach and Tom (my precious grandfather) was involved

with the North U/19 team in volunteer position as Property Steward Assistant. So, the Ryan family has all the teams covered, and we were featured in a photo and a story in the Club newsletter "North News" in 1990.

What was becoming increasingly prevalent in my life at that stage was my love of the history of the club and collecting any sort of club memorabilia (Football Records, Footy Cards, Membership Tickets, Medallions, Club Functions Menu's, basically anything that was connected to North). But my favorite part of the week was between 5.00pm – 6.30pm on a Tuesday and Thursday night when I would stand in front of the Grandstand watching training with my Grandfather and Uncle Paddy, who were part of a dozen older supporters who were known as the "Unofficial Selectors". They all had been following North all their lives and I loved nothing more than hearing them wax lyrical of the old days and comparing North players from their day to the present. It was not uncommon for some players to yell out from the ground while there was training "did I get a game this week?" It was a priceless banter that I loved.

I held the position of Reserve Grade Team Manager for 5 years, but in early 1992, my priorities in life had changed as I had been recently married. An opportunity arose in the Westpac Bank where I could be appointed to after-hours work servicing Automatic Telling Machines (ATM's) every third weekend, which meant being "on-call" for all the weekend. The wage was too good to refuse and as my wife and I had recently purchased our own house, the financial impacts outweighed my volunteer position as Team Manager, so I took the after-hours job and had to resign my position at North.

Even though I missed the inner sanctum experience, I could now pick up my grandparents and uncle and take them to the footy every week and be able to sit with them and the "unofficial selectors". When I was the Team Manager I had to be on my best behavior as I represented the club and not be the lunatic supporter I used to be. Now the shackles were off. I resumed shouting and barracking as I used to and my family wondered how such a quiet, mild mannered person could change into this madman at the football. My wife was very embarrassed by the way I was at the footy and she ended up not going with me, other than Grand Finals. She was quite happy to wave goodbye to me from the front door on game day and not have to accompany me! Needless to say, I'm not proud of the way I used to carry-on.

I would lose count how many times my Nan would yell out "Greg, sit down" during a game when I would let my emotions get the better of me. I now believe, perhaps unjustifiably, that it was my only way of releasing the anxieties and frustrations I had with my IA. Living with my secret was increasingly taking more of an emotional toll on me and footy was my only outlet: hence my boorish behavior.

With our new house, I could do something that I had always wanted, and that was to create a "North Shrine" of my own where I could put on display all my framed pictures, posters and memorabilia. As we had a 3-bedroom house I converted one of these bedrooms into my own museum and all the available wall space was covered. My wife knew it was a passion of mine (although we would now agree it was more of an obsession), but she was quite happy to indulge me. I used to love showing off my North room when anyone visited.

When I purchased my first personal computer, I even spent more of my spare time in my North room, as I started to catalogue all my memorabilia on spreadsheets and would create my own databases of player's information etc.

It was during this time I started to frequent Collectable Fairs in an endeavor to add to my North collection, which I still do to this day. My North collection has been a work in progress and is my most precious personal possession. I would hate to imagine how much money I've spent purchasing items, but it's never been a monetary asset to me, and I will never sell any of it. No amount of money could give me the enjoyment my collection provides. My collection has been bequeathed to my nephews and I hope in years to come they will do same to their children.

When my world fell apart in 2001 and I had to rely on my family and doctors to get me through, the one thing that made me feel healthy again was my love of North and it made me voluntarily get out of bed to go to the footy on a weekend. Just as I used North as my outlet from all my physical issues as a child, I was now using North as my outlet to cope with my mental issues.

It was different for me when I went to the footy however and to everyone I seemed more settled and rational. I would barrack as passionately as ever, but I would not lose control as I once had.

The thing that had changed was the heavy medications which now controlled my emotions.

When I was at my lowest ebb during that time, the North family came to my rescue and embraced me like I had always embraced

it. When the opportunity of a part-time position was offered to me at the end of 2002, it was the start of a new life for me and then once again in 2017.

When I was married, my wife used to say that she "didn't marry me, she

married the North Melbourne Football Club", and I used to just laugh, but deep-down I probably knew she was right. North was the only thing in my life where I could feel normal and not feel shamed or inadequate.

It is not a traditional love story but perhaps my true love and the agency that has subtly supported me through many of my travails, quite often unconsciously, just happens to be **my** club, the North Melbourne Football Club!

Glossary – One Boy's Medical History

- 1964 - (1-day old) - Transverse Colostomy Surgery (Melbourne Royal Children's Hospital – RCH – 34 days)
- 1964 - (3 months) - Infection - Non-surgical –   (RCH - 6 days)
- 1964 – (5 months) - Infection, Excoriation & Dilatation of Colostomy - Non-Surgical (RCH – 15 days)
- 1965 - (18 months) - Anorectoplasty – Pull Through Surgery (RCH – 22 days)
- 1966 - (21 months) - Closure of Colostomy Surgery (RCH - 19 days)
- 1967 - (2 years) - Penis Surgery (Excision of Penile Pit & Polyp)
- 1967 - (2 years 1 month) - Trimming of Redundant Rectal Mucosa & Rectal Wall Surgery (RCH – 18 days)
- 1969 - (5 years 1 month) - Removal of Mass of Faecal Dis-impaction Surgery (RCH - 6 days)
- 1970 - (6 years 5 months) -Right Undescended Testicle Orchidopexy Surgery (RCH – 8 days)
- 1971 - (7 years 1 month) - Left Undescended Testicle Orchidopexy Surgery (RCH – 8 days)
- 1975 – (9 years 10 months) - Cystoscopy - (RCH- 1 day)
- 1986 (aged 22) - Torsion of Testes (Twisted testicles) Surgery – (Moorabbin Hospital – 4 days)
- 1993 - July (aged 29) - Emergency Removal of Appendix Surgery (Cabrini Hospital – 4 days)
- 1999 - November (aged 35) - Corrective surgery on Anus (Oversewing of Prolapsing of Rectal Mucosa) – (Cabrini -1 day)
- 2001 – April (aged 36) – Nervous Breakdown (Ainslie Hospital)
- 2001 – July (aged 37) –Nervous Breakdown Relapse (Ainslie Hospital)
- 2002 – January (aged 37) – Removal of all Varicose Veins Surgery from Left leg (Monash Hospital - 2 days)

- 2002 – January (aged 37) - Emergency Room Hospital procedure due to Severe Constipation & Burst Blood vessel in Prostate - Non-surgical (Epworth Hospital)
- 2007 - October (aged 43) - Corrective surgery on Anus (Oversewing of Prolapsing of Rectal Mucosa) - (Cabrini Hospital – 3 days)
- 2015 – May (aged 51) - Corrective surgery on Anus (Prolapsing of Rectal Mucosa) "This time my Surgeon performed a new procedure called "Transanal Haemorrhoidal Dearterialsation & Mucosopexy" (Cabrini Hospital – 2 days)
- 2015 – May (aged 51) - Colonoscopy (Cabrini Hospital)
- 2015 – October (aged 51) - Flexible Cystoscopy & Prostate examination – Non-surgical tests (Box Hill Hospital - 2 days)
- 2015 – October (aged 51) - Corrective surgery on Anus (Oversewing of Prolapsing of Rectal Mucosa) – (Cabrini Hospital – 2 days)
- 2016 - March (aged 51) - Flexible Sigmoidoscopy; Anorectal Ultrasound; Rectal Manometry & Pudendal Nerve Studies (Re: Sacral Nerve Stimulation)
- Non-surgical tests (Warringal Private Hospital - 1 day)
- 2018 - October (aged 54) Corrective surgery on Anus (Oversewing of Prolapsing of Rectal Mucosa) – (Cabrini Hospital – 3 days)

Rarity: I have had 24 medical interventions and spent 171 days of my life admitted in a Hospital for surgeries, tests and care. The following incidence rates give an indication of how extremely fortunate I was with my rare congenital conditions to have been born in Melbourne, Australia and be the under care of the Royal Children's Hospital:

- Imperforate Anus/Anorectal Malformation –1: 5,000 (My type Rectal/Anal Agenesis without Fistula, less than 1: 100,000)
- Undescended Testicles – 5 % of boys born
- Webbed toes – 1: 2,500
- Torsion of Testicles – 1: 4000 in a male less than 25 of years of age

ACKNOWLEDGMENTS

To be able to complete this book and go to places I never imagined, I had an amazing family and friends who encouraged and supported me. I want to acknowledge these special people. These range from the Advisory Committee members who have given up time to support the building of the One in 5000 Foundation; to fellow members of the IA/ARM community across the world; to members of parliament, like the wonderful Senator Anne Urquhart who read into the Australian parliamentary procedures the work we had been doing and became the first parliamentarian in the world to ever mention our plight.

I also wish to mention my amazing doctors, the individuals at North Melbourne Football Club, my friends and family, organisations such as Continence Foundation of Australia, the Victorian Dept. of Health, the Pull-Thru Network USA, the

various printers and distributors across the globe and agents for helping with all arms of our ambitious programs.

Thank you one and all, but most of all I owe everything to the love of mum & dad and as I now say, that's never been a secret.

COLORECTAL SURGEONS COMMENTS

From: **Dr Marc Levitt Chief of Colorectal & Pelvic Reconstruction Surgery Nationwide Children's Hospital, Columbus Ohio USA**

"It is a great honor to have been asked to give my thoughts about this work by Greg Ryan, an inspiring figure in the effort to improve the lives of patients born with colorectal problems. Greg was born in 1964 with a complex anorectal malformation and received care at the Melbourne Royal Children Hospital by two of the founders of the field of pediatric colorectal surgery, Douglas Stephens and Justin Kelly.

From my view Greg is a "walking museum" who can illustrate to hundreds of clinicians what a patient can go through, what challenges exist for caregivers, and how our efforts on improving the quality of life of our patients over their lifetime can take shape. Greg's willingness to share his story represents unique altruism, as he knows that if he can affect clinicians in a positive way he can inspire them to do better for their patients.

Recently Greg rose to speak an audience of 250 surgeons and nurses gathered from 53 countries...at the first consortium meeting addressing colorectal challenges. He has what I like to call "moral authority", a power that so many patients and their families possess. He recognizes that it is his unique responsibility to tell clinicians what patients need, and to convince them that they need to ask their patients "what can we do for you to improve your lives."

From: **Associate Professor Sebastian King Paediatric Colorectal Surgeon Melbourne Royal Children's Hospital**

"Since meeting Greg in 2015, I have been humbled by his past and energised by his plans for the future. His commitment to raising awareness for children and adults affected by Anorectal Malformations is inspiring. I hope that our

work together may continue to improve the lives of patients and families across Victoria and Australia."

A Final Word

On the 19th January 2019, a 10-year-old boy named Seven Charles Thomas Bridges from Kentucky USA, who was born with Imperforate Anus, tragically took his own life, as a result of being repeatedly bullied at school and being told "he stinks" because he couldn't control his bowel movements. In his mother's words "Twenty-six surgeries from the day my son was born. Twenty-six surgeries. He just wanted to be normal, that's all".

The stigma and bullying attached to IA/ARM has to stop now. Seven's life cannot be in vain. Parents must be provided with greater information from Doctors to share with educators. The public must be made aware of this congenital condition.

Made in the USA
Monee, IL
02 October 2023

43856536R00116